PERGAMON GENERAL PSYCHOLOGY SERIES

Editors: Arnold P. Goldstein, *Syracuse University*
Leonard A. Krasner, *SUNY, Stony Brook*

PHYSICAL DISABILITY
and
HUMAN BEHAVIOR

PHYSICAL DISABILITY
and
HUMAN BEHAVIOR

by

James W. McDaniel, Ph.D.

University of Colorado
School of Medicine
Denver, Colorado

PERGAMON PRESS

New York • Toronto • Oxford • London • Mexico City
Edinburgh • Sydney • Braunschweig • Buenos Aires

PERGAMON PRESS INC.
Maxwell House, Fairview Park, Elmsford, N.Y. 10523

PERGAMON OF CANADA LTD.
207 Queen's Quay West, Toronto 117, Ontario

PERGAMON PRESS LTD.
Headington Hill Hall, Oxford;
4 & 5 Fitzroy Square, London W.1.

PERGAMON PRESS S.A.
Villalongin 32, Mexico 5, D.F.

PERGAMON PRESS (SCOTLAND) LTD.
2 & 3 Teviot Place, Edinburgh 1

PERGAMON PRESS (AUST.) PTY. LTD.
Ruschutters Bay, Sydney, N.S.W.

VIEWEG & SOHN GmbH
Burgplatz 1, Braunschweig

08 006866 9

Contents

CONTENTS

Foreword

THE PAST decade has witnessed a deepening interest on the part of research psychologists in the area of physical disability and its concomitant behavior. With the development of numerous university programs designed to train counselors, teachers, social workers and physicians in the skills and theories of adjustment to disability, this interest has intensified. Despite the growing awareness of the importance of this field of endeavor, there has been no single source to which the student could turn for a survey of pertinent theories and research approaches. This book corrects the shortcoming. It provides compact, yet comprehensive, summaries of theoretical foundations and incorporates existing research findings. It is written at a level of difficulty that is appropriate for both undergraduate and graduate instruction. The student, or researcher, reading this volume can secure a detailed awareness of theory, and, at the same time, can prepare himself to read original sources with more appreciation and greater facility.

The author, James W. McDaniel, is eminently qualified to write such a text. He has served as a rehabilitation counselor, completed his doctoral work in a Rehabilitation Counselor Training Program, worked as the Director of Research for the Rehabilitation Agency of the State of Ohio for several years, and is currently Assistant Professor of Physical Medicine at the University of Colorado School of Medicine in Denver. He speaks, therefore, from the viewpoint of experience in service and research, as well as from academic interest.

It is with pride that I recommend this book to Rehabilitation
Counselor Educators as a potential textbook for the course,
Psychology of Disability. Researchers interested in the field
will find this survey valuable and intriguing.

BEATRIX COBB Ph.D., *Director*
Rehabilitation Counseling Training
Texas Technological College
Lubbock, Texas

Preface

THE INITIAL urge for the writing of this book was the need for documentation with objective findings, in my personal teaching and research, of the major psychological variables effected by the processes of physical illness and disability. First as a student and then as a teacher and investigator, I have been impressed with the abundance of literature on the problem which, unfortunately for my purposes, contains almost entirely opinion, case studies, and descriptive reports and surveys. Such information, while instructive at a popular level, is not scientifically reliable for the most part. The major textbooks concerning the psychological aspects of physical illness and disability, too, are descriptive and deal in detail mainly with social consequences. There has never been a source to which one could go to determine what answers research has provided in this field of study in regard to the interaction of psychological processes and the processes of treatment and rehabilitation.

To pursue a psychological problem in relation to physical factors now requires covering a great deal of information in a number of technical fields in rehabilitation including medicine, vocational rehabilitation, occupational therapy, physical therapy, speech pathology, psychology, sociology, social work as well as other specialties and subspecialties. Each discipline has its own need for psychological constructs, information and research. Clearly, behavioral science is the prime interface of these related technologies which, I maintain, do not differ in principle in respect to the rehabilitation of disabled individuals, only in technology. I felt convinced then that some attempt should be made to synthesize and communicate in a concise volume the most reliable and scientifically sound conclusions available from the literature of these disciplines which should be of common value and interest, and would provide a realistic and substantial base for the education of students in fields involved in rehabilitation.

It became clear, once the present work had begun, that even the scientific literature in rehabilitation fields covering many approaches to illness, disability, treatment and rehabilitation would not always provide definitive conclusions. The quality and reliability of psychological studies had to be judged as well, narrowing an already limited amount of information. Many gaps remain to be filled by future investigators. On the other hand, it seemed to me that studies from specialties such as industrial and physiological psychology are seldom brought to bear in our work, although having considerable applicability and perhaps more solid clinical value than either psychopathology or social psychology. Therefore, in the belief that available *objective* information, although diverse and difficult to synthesize, should be substituted for the folklore and generalities that have been propagated for generations, this volume has been written.

The reader will become aware, however, that what at first seems to be a global approach to the question has many self-imposed limitations. Restrictions have been made to bring the problems as sharply into focus as possible based upon the available research. First, I have dealt foremost with individual psychological changes which result from changes in physiological functioning through illness and permanent disablement. This largely precludes congenital impairments which are accommodated developmentally, though not without psychological consequences. Second, the reader will find an obvious lack of attention to psychopathology or personality traits or patterns as is frequently found in the literature. I believe that approach has been notable in its feeble contribution to understanding the problems involved. Third, and most important, psychological processes are the primary divisions for discussion with diagnostic or etiological divisions only incidental to the illumination of the effects of changes in physiological functioning upon psychological functioning. In every case, implications for treatment and for comprehensive rehabilitation are included. No thorough coverage has been given the extensive investigations of complex problems such as brain damage and deafness in this fundamental text. They have a substantial literature of their own encompassing many possible variations, and the student desiring specialized, detailed information on such physical disabilities will find several excellent and recent resources available.

As a logical beginning to the material, a brief overview of several of the most prominent theories attempting to explain the relationships between behavior and physiological functioning is provided. Of course, there are more, some worth the student's time to explore further, and some not. It is merely to be pointed out that our studies are not without some theoretical foundation even though presently far from sufficient.

Next is presented the more precise studies, and the conclusions to be derived therefrom, concerning attitudes in relation to illness and disability. I have drawn certain distinctions concerning differing viewpoints and methods of studying attitudes toward the disabled that need airing, together with pointing out that attitudes toward physical impairments and disabling conditions appear to be separable from attitudes toward disabled persons. For the sake of discussion, studies of the attitudes of employers and of family members are treated apart from public attitudes. The values and attitudes demonstrated by patients and clients themselves are best considered under the subsequent headings of Perception, Emotional Reactions, and Motivation.

The chapter on emotions presented innumerable possibilities for discussion, but the choice was made to confine the discussion first of all to the evidence concerning emotional reactions to the conditions of illness, situational stresses, institutionalization, treatment and rehabilitation. Second, physical factors important in determining emotional response, such as pain, have been analyzed. Two most commonly encountered emotional responses, which may also be described as defensive reactions, depression and denial, are also examined in detail. All of these factors may, of course, be expected to be operative regardless of diagnosis or disability category.

The section on sensory and perceptual factors, too, will be found to deal exclusively with evidence concerning central issues, or largely common variables. Included is a considerable amount of research related to bodily perceptions and the so-called "body-image," the phantom sensations and explanations of their occurrence, and information related to compensation for loss of sensory input. Two especially applicable perceptual theories, Werner and Wapner's Sensory-Tonic theory, and Karl Smith's Neurogeometric theory are also discussed.

Both "motivation" and "learning" are quite important psychological variables in relation to physical illness and disability and, like emotion and perception, are arbitrarily denoted systems of the process of central regulation and control. Both rubrics are too broad and potentially encompass too vast an array of behavior to be considered without rather sharp limitations. Therefore, rather special definitions of both motivation and learning have been employed herein to cover those variables which will most likely be of common concern to students of all technological approaches to illness and disability. Motivation is thus discussed, presenting information selected as most relevant, in relation to performance, ability, the direction and magnitude of the patient's efforts, and outcome or achievement.

Learning, as a special functional class of behavior, is likewise selectively limited to the knowledge available relevant to the acquisition and modification of means of control by the organism itself over its own systems and its environment. The learning of skills has therefore been chosen as the central issue. Skill implies intrinsic mastery, finely coordinated regulation and control of essential systems, the implications being the same whether the skills of interest are those necessary for ambulation or for occupational performance. The findings of research in this regard should be of immediate value in many aspects of rehabilitation, if not all.

In dealing primarily with central issues and more general psychological processes and variables in relation to illness, treatment, and ultimately rehabilitation, it is hoped that at last the common ground for many rehabilitation disciplines will have been found. The objective has been to provide a selective but generalizable foundation for students in a variety of related fields who will find it indispensable to understand the mechanisms of human behavior as related to their efforts with individuals for whom they are charged with considerable responsibility. This responsibility requires judgment, and judgment requires knowledge.

Some of the personal research which appears in this book was supported, in part, by a Research and Training Center Grant (RT-10) from the Social and Rehabilitation Service, Department of Health, Education, and Welfare, Washington, D.C. Gratitude is also due Mrs. Jean Clyne for typing and proofreading the manuscript, and to a number of friends, associates and students who have contributed in one way or another to the ideas expressed.

JAMES W. McDANIEL, Ph.D.

Chapter 1

THEORETICAL FOUNDATIONS

THE HISTORY of psychology has recorded several attempts
to correlate the anatomical characteristics of man with his
behavior. These have ranged from the humoral notions of
Hippocrates, the "Father of Medicine," to the phrenology of
Gall and, in more recent times, elaborate systems were developed for relating personality types to physique. Since none
of these has satisfied the need for explaining relationships
between "mind" and "body" and offer little, if any, relevant
information for the practice of rehabilitation, a brief resume
of contemporary theory will be of greater interest, and will
provide the student with something of a framework within
which to evaluate the material to be presented in subsequent
chapters.

The need for the study and application of psychological
principles in relation to chronic illness and disability is well
accepted in rehabilitation. The influence of psychology is
today apparent, at least marginally, in the education of all
relatively new specialties and professions involved in rehabilitation such as rehabilitation counseling, physical medicine, physical therapy, occupational therapy, speech therapy and social
work. It is the nature of these fields to emphasize training in

1

all aspects of patient care and therapeutic relationships and, hence, psychology. For these professionals, an accurate up-to-date accounting of the behavioral knowledge in rehabilitation and the psychological response of the chronically ill and disabled is difficult to obtain in this rapidly developing area of study. Most contemporary sources of information contain primarily collections of anecdotes, opinions, and case studies, or are very general descriptions of the supposed characteristics of frequently encountered disability categories. Enough investigation has now been accomplished, however, that the student need not depend wholly upon such information, but can instead take a more objective and critical look at the psychological responses of his patient, not only to his condition, but also to the treatment process. First of all, however, some appreciation of the major theoretical principles and positions popular in the psychology of chronic illness and disability is necessary. The first two are theories of individual behavior, whereas the others are principally social psychological theories.

ADLER'S INDIVIDUAL PSYCHOLOGY

One of the earlier theorists of the current era was Alfred Adler (1870-1937) who is largely responsible for the ubiquitous preoccupation with "inferiority feelings" in rehabilitation and individual psychology. Adler was educated in medicine in Vienna and after practicing opthalmology and general medicine turned his attention to psychiatry. He originated the modern psychological school of thought known as "Individual psychology" which stressed the uniqueness of the human personality. Adler's psychology, which developed at about the same time, departed from classical psychoanalysis in its emphasis on social urges and individual uniqueness in which he assumed man to be motivated primarily by social rather than sexual impulses. The most notable of Adler's concepts, in regard to the physically disabled, are the striving for superiority, inferiority feelings, compensation and style of life.

The unifying concept which assures consistency in personality and behavior is, according to Adler, the striving for superiority. By this, Adler meant not a sort of "superiority complex" as is commonly supposed, but rather a pervasive effort and direction to behavior and personality development towards self-realization or self-actualization. To Adler, the striving for superiority was innate, the essence of life itself, and the urge which moves human beings from one developmental stage to another, as the source of all drives and motivation. Adler's studies recounted the infinite variety of ways in which individuals may express this central force in life; but the major recurrent theme to be found in his writings is that all behavior is goal-directed, and that there is a definite concrete mode of achieving or attempting to achieve perfection in some realm which he called the individual's style of life. Adler (1927) used as illustration the very early phantasies of children to make this concept clear. He stated, "He who wishes to recognize the nature of this goal, should watch a child at play, at optionally selected occupations or when phantasying about his future profession. The apparent change in these phenomena is purely external for in every new goal the child imagines a predetermined triumph" (p. 14).

Developmentally, the theory of individual psychology points out that the child possesses a feeling of inferiority in relation to his parents and the world in general. This is the origin of the striving for superiority. Adler stated, "Thus, the child arrives at the positing of a goal, an imagined goal of superiority, whereby his poverty is transformed into wealth, his subordination into domination, his suffering into happiness and pleasure, his ignorance into omniscience and his incapacity into artistic creation" (p. 14). In relation to disability, Adler's assumption was that the longer and more intensely insecurity and dependency are felt, the more suffering is imposed because of physical or mental weaknesses, and the more acutely the person becomes aware of life's neglect or misfortunes, the higher the goal of superiority is placed and the more rigidly it will be pursued. Carried to its extremes, Adler says, "Every neurosis can be understood as an attempt to free oneself from a feeling of inferiority in order to gain a feeling of superiority" (p. 23). The analysis follows that the exemptions and privileges of illness and disability may provide a substitute for the original goal of superiority, i.e., the manipulation and domination of others.

An early notion of Adler's was that of "organ inferiority" and overcompensation, attempting to explain the reason for afflictions to a particular region of the body. This concept has been a fertile one for psychosomatic medicine, but seems to hold little promise for the psychology of disability. The fundamental idea was that there was often a basic inferiority in one region or organ due to developmental or genetic abnormality. Moreover, the person with a defective organ attempts to compensate for the weakness by strengthening it. Later, Adler's concept became broadened to include psychological and social handicaps as well as physical impairments, i.e., imperfection in any sphere of life.

Such dynamics as the striving for superiority and compensation for inferiority were not intended to be taken to be abnormal, although they could become so. It was Adler's contention that these elements of human development were the ultimate cause of all improvement in man's lot. Man is thus able to overcome inferiority and at the same time be drawn forward by the striving for superiority. Very early in childhood, a style of life develops which, according to Adler, is each person's own unique way of striving toward the common "goal of superiority." Throughout life, then, the individual selects and assimilates those experiences which fit his style of life and ignores the rest. New ways of expression are attained, and old ones discarded, but the style of life remains the same.

Physical or mental deformities were considered principal causes of a "faulty" life style.

The study of human behavior owes a considerable debt to Adler and to his followers for promoting the conceptions of the uniqueness of the individual's development and behavior patterns, and the emphasis upon the goal-directedness of behavior. However, at the same time, specifically in rehabilitation fields, it is found that some of his concepts such as compensation and inferiority are not only applied indiscriminately, but seem to have reached proportions of usage which might qualify as "laws of disability", as if they might be characteristic only of persons with physical imperfections as reflections of neuroticism. Most likely, one could find just as legitimate an argument for supporting the proposition that those who choose to devote their professional or personal lives to work with the disabled show about the same characteristics, psychologically speaking, as their patients.

While no one is likely to seriously deny the appeal of Adler's mechanisms, there is reason to suspect the pervasiveness with which they are applied. In Wright's (1960) analysis of the mechanism of inferiority in the disabled, little convincing evidence was found except to indicate that it is frequently a characteristic "assigned" to the disabled by others. Some specific research in this connection will be evaluated in a later section, but in general it seems that the relationship between disability and inferiority is not as inviolate as is typically assumed. Wright, in her appraisal, also states, "In only one sense would we propose that compensation as a principle of mental hygiene has anything to recommend it. The driving force that pushes a person to new pursuits may produce major alterations in the individual's system of values" (p. 51). In regard to the mechanism of inferiority, Wright has interpreted correctly, as Adler would have, that imperfection in any sphere of living is capable of giving rise to feelings of inferiority, not simply a physical impairment. It is even more likely that the basis for inferiority may have existed before the onset of disability. Much research could be done in this theoretical framework in the field of rehabilitation, and might be particularly promising from the standpoint of the style of life in relation to disability, both congenital and acquired. Presumably, style of life is influenced by resources and opportunity, and several questions seem worthwhile investigating.

Some rigorous studies of compensation might produce helpful information. It may well be, as Wright has implied, that compensation leads to a shift in values. After all, a person values his bits of success much more than his failures and tends to exploit avenues which have produced success in the past. This notion of compensation is not without considerable meaning in all of human behavior, not just in rehabilitation. However, a conception based upon the definition of compensation as a shift in values will not always suit the situation. There are several meanings of the term "compensation" in use today which must somehow be clarified. Too, there is a great deal of folklore related to compensation which confuses the issue terribly.

Compensation for the loss of a sensory system, for example, is probably accomplished, not through some mystical development or increased sensitivity of the remaining systems, but through a shift in attention which selects previously unused cues obtainable via the open channels. Compensation, as a construct, should basically be the same for any aspect of deprivation. The deprivation basis of any sensory loss is readily apparent and has nothing whatever to do with any value system the individual may have.

In our appraisal of Adler's contribution to the psychology of disability, we must state that the theory has been greatly misused and distorted in rehabilitation work. This might have been justified had it improved the practice of rehabilitation, but their violations seem only to have confused the issues of dealing with the behavioral difficulties of the disabled individual. It is not the fault of the theory, however.

There is ample, though not well documented, evidence that disability may in fact contribute to a person's striving for superiority in that he can behave in ways and control others that he ordinarily could not. This has been practiced freely by disabled rehabilitation workers from time to time, in manipulating everyone from clients to legislators. It should, therefore, come as no surprise and cause no indignant alarm that a disabled person who has not otherwise been able to capitalize on his condition may use his affliction as a means of control and of achieving his own ends, emotionally as well as socially and perhaps even economically. In the final analysis, Adler's theory may offer us little means for understanding the general relationship of disability to behavior, but if this were the criteria for inclusion, the chapter would not have been necessary at all.

SCHILDER'S BODY-IMAGE

A hypothetical concept which has been almost as popular with rehabilitation workers as inferiority is that of the body-image and its disruption due to chronic illness and disability. We owe this concept to the early observations of Sir Henry Head who described what he chose to call the "postural schema" of the body. More familiar and more recent, however, are the writings of Paul Schilder (1950), which originally appeared in 1935, in which he elaborates at length his notions concerning the development and importance of the body-image interpreted within the framework of psychoanalytic symbolism. In defining what is meant by body-image, Schilder emphasized the role of all sources of sensation and spatial relationships of the body in contributing to what he considered to be that most fundamental of all human experience. The perception and representation of the body-image is not necessarily conscious even though much of behavior and perception are said to be determined by it. The concept of body-image is difficult to express, as shown in Schilder's struggle to reach some understanding himself.

> We may call it 'body-image'. The term indicated that we are not dealing with a mere sensation or imagination. There is a self-appearance of the body. It indicates also that, although it has come through the senses, it is not a mere perception. There are mental pictures and representations involved in it, but it is not mere representation (p. 11).

In spite of the vagueness compounded by psychoanalytic interpretation in Schilder's views, foremost credit is given to the postural and tactile impressions, visual sensation, and spatial relationships of one's own body in the construction of a body concept which is an essential aspect of behavior. Recent years have seen a considerable amount of writing and research in the literature of disability based upon the idea of the body-image and that of disruption or distortion due to disease or impairment. This has been especially true in regard to the study of the effects of amputation.

Schilder himself remarked upon body-image distortions in a number of conditions including hemiplegia and amputation, and has said in general of the effects of disease or injury:

> There arises the problem of organic disease in connection with the postural model of the body. Organic disease provokes abnormal sensations; it immediately changes the image of the body, partly the picture side of it and partly the libidinous investment. These sensations immediately become a part of the general attitude and experience of the individual . . . (p. 181).

There is much literature to the effect that chronic illness produces some change in the patient's inferred body-image, but none whatever that this has any relation to his adjustment, recovery, and rehabilitation. In essence, body-image seems best conceived as an element of the self-concept rather than an explanation for behavior in itself. If one assumes rather that the self-concept derives from the external and internal environments, and includes a definitive body-image, a more realistic perspective is attained.

The most interesting and promising application of the body-image concept at the present time lies in its use by some as an explanation for phantom sensations. This will be discussed in the sections dealing with sensory and perceptual problems. In general, we might state at this point that while body-image is a useful concept, its exact contribution may necessarily be limited to some very specific problems.

PARSONS' SOCIAL ROLE THEORY

An important recent trend of thought which is relevant to the study of psychological responses to disability and rehabilitation is exemplified by the theories of Talcott Parsons. Parsons' (1958) essay on *Definitions of Health and Illness in the Light of American Values and Social Structure* may be taken as representing a conceptual framework which may be helpful in our area of concern. The assumptions based upon Parsons' conceptions that may be applied here are:

1. "Role" is an individual's performance of various differentiated tasks within his own social system.

2. Illness or disability produces incapacity and therefore limits or inhibits the performance of accustomed tasks.

3. Health, conversely, represents a state of optimum capacity for the performance of valued tasks.

4. Likewise, rehabilitation operationally refers to any treatment or service which is designed to restore or at least optimize the person's capacity for appropriate role performance.

5. Illness or disability, furthermore, disrupts the role patterns

of the family (the most fundamental social system to which an individual may belong) and its permanence leads to a reorganization of the fundamental social system of the family.

The assumptions above concerning the individual effects of illness or disability, however, only really begin to take on meaning when we consider the social structure and values of American society, as Parsons most aptly points out. Parsons writes that every society has a concern and control of the capacities of its members so that it operates to forestall or to rectify disturbances in capacity. The elaborate and expensive governmental agencies set up specifically for this purpose testify to the concern and control that must be exercised.

In regard to American values Parsons has made some very interesting points, among them that within this system "health" is clearly a natural state and "illness" a deviation, albeit involuntary. The sick or disabled may not, therefore, be held accountable for their condition which may, in fact, have resulted from their own negligence. This does not mean that society makes no demands of the individual in this situation. Quite the contrary. As Parsons has explained, a definite ritual performance is demanded of the sick, dictated by American values. First of all, the sick or injured must subject themselves to the proper treatment institutionally prescribed for those in such a state. Illness, then, is in itself a socially institutionalized role. This role being based upon the concept of "involuntary incapacity" has certain basic features. These are, according to Parsons, that illness entitles a person, within limits, to exemption from usual role demands. Illness and disability are conditionally sanctioned contingent upon the individual's recognition that his state is inherently undesirable (a deviation) and upon his realization that he must cooperate with others and seek help. That there is very little flexibility in these role demands in American values will immediately come to mind when one considers his own experiences with persons who have not fulfilled some aspect of the role. The "sick role" simply does not suit some persons, for whatever reason; others submit reluctantly, but some welcome the role. There are probably very real age and sex differences in this regard.

Health and education, in Parsons' scheme of things, appear to be valued as the basis for the capacity for independent achievement and economic productivity. Achievement capacity is developed through education and protected or restored by health services. This succinctly describes the American system, at least for most classes, but unfortunately is not a good guiding principle by which to study individual psychological effects of illness and disability. Nevertheless, one can see a great deal of promise in the social role approach to disability. Even though insufficient research has been accomplished to permit more than empirical approval, the role performance of the disabled person, his family patterns, and the publicly held attitudes of various groups have been the recent interests of some researchers.

SOMATOPSYCHOLOGY

Somatopsychology is another contemporary social-psychological approach which has been applied to physical illness and disability (Barker, *et al.* 1946; Wright, 1960). It has been defined as the study of "those variations in physique that affect the psychological situation of a person by influencing the effectiveness of his body as a tool for actions or by serving as a stimulus to himself or others" (Barker, p. 1). Several elements of this theory have become understandably popular in rehabilitation, if not well substantiated by research results. Perhaps oversimplified, the basic tenet of somatopsychology seems to be that physique and behavior are interrelated and mutually dependent. Behavioral incapacities and social rejection place the disabled in a subordinate position where many goals are inaccessible. At that, persons with mild or invisible disabilities suffer greater frustration and maladjustment than more severely disabled because social expectations are more strenuous for them and yet they may be unable to perform.

Wright has devoted the final chapter of her book to an assessment of somatopsychology up to that time, and has concluded, "Inconsistency is fairly typical of the status of many of the findings in the field of somatopsychology" (p. 371), and that, "Somatic abnormality as a physical fact is not linked in a direct or simple way to psychological behavior" (p. 373). It is safe to say, furthermore, that the status of somatopsychology has not changed recently. Wright arrived at some general conclusions based on her assessment of the results of psychological research prior to 1960. What she had generalized then is still quite true. Wright's summary, in part, is as follows:

1. There is no substantial indication that persons with an impaired physique differ *as a group* in their *general or overall adjustment.*
2. There is also no clear evidence of an association between types of physical disability and particular personality characteristics.
3. Although personality patterns have not been found consistently to distinguish disability groups as a whole, certain behaviors rather directly connected with the limitations have.
4. Public, verbalized attitudes toward persons with disabilities are on the average mildly favorable (pp. 373-7).

These generalizations, unfortunately, leave us with no real appreciation for the value of the scientific study of the behavioral aspects of chronic illness and disability, much less for the somatopsychological approach. However, a great deal more can be said on the subject now in light of recent research. Let us, therefore, consider in more detail some of the major points of somatopsychology.

An important and widely embraced principle of behavior

espoused by Barker *et al.* and by Wright is that of "mourning" or depression and the acceptance of loss. In general, this theory supposes that mourning for a lost function or part is inevitable and is equated with realization of the reality of the loss and facilitates recovery and acceptance of disability, while denial is the antithesis and interferes with rehabilitation. According to Wright, "There is good reason to believe that the period of mourning can be a healing period during which the wound is first anesthetized and then gradually closed, leaving the least scarring" (p. 114). However, Wright recognized that the "Psychological value of mourning" is yet to be confirmed.

The mourning reaction has been characterized most clearly and concisely by Wright (1955). Serious illness or disability is accompanied by a constriction of psychological awareness and experience "down to the skin" and is expressed by despair, depression, and emotional withdrawal. Any change (new situation) is brought immediately and sharply into predominant focus and unimpaired capabilities are ignored during mourning. Preoccupation with the loss is primary and all else is secondary, this being accentuated by the desire to maintain the self-concept and body-image intact. There is also a "requirement of mourning" which demands that the patient show proper respect for his loss and for the gravity of his situation. Any other response is considered to be inappropriate behavior according to the values of society. The gradual abatement of mourning occurs following the reconstruction of the body-image and self-concept to accommodate changes and the reestablishment of a sense of personal worth.

Two related and popular principles of the somatopsychological approach are "devaluation" and "spread". Devaluation refers to the attitude of others as well as the disabled person himself of lowered esteem. This is shown in various ways: by prejudice against the disabled similar to that shown other minorities, by prejudged helplessness and dependency, and by attitudes of overprotection or rejection. The disabled person's own attitude may reflect "devaluation" of his own position which may also include the phenomenon of "spread." By this is meant that the disability may not remain confined to the actual limits of the impairment; instead, the individual may come to view himself as being incapacitated in additional ways. In other words, he may become excessively disabled.

This brief discussion does not take into account all of the concepts and variations of the somatopsychological approach by any means, but as Wright herself has stated, "There is much room for further conceptual clarification. Some of the explanatory concepts will prove expendable under the critical scrutiny of research. Others will take their place. Some will become more fruitful as the precision of their definitions is increased" (1960, p. 379-80). The student is cautioned simply to study somatopsychology (Wright, 1960) with the reservation in mind that this has not been presented as a body of knowledge but as guide to further study. It is largely an outline of suggested principles of the psychological aspects of physical disability which have been illustrated by an interesting collection of anecdotal records.

An overview of the major theoretical foundations of the study of the psychological aspects of physical disability and chronic illness must lead to the conclusion that while we are not devoid of a rationale for our studies, the progress of research and education in rehabilitation fields has definitely been impeded by a relatively weak foundation. In addition, the fact that such an overabundance of largely unfounded opinion and folklore exists in the field makes the job of getting at the facts even more formidable. Nowhere in the literature of any endeavor is there to be found such a great amount of material with such little evidence to support it. Nowhere in any field is there to be found such unreliable information and poorly conceived and executed "research." But the professions involved in rehabilitation have not yet reached a state of maturity which demands more exacting and precise information.

They are still primarily concerned with "practical problems." Only recently has concern been expressed with the need to get the available research and knowledge into the educational process and to the practictioner. It should be suggested to those who are concerned with this problem that much of this information is of such quality and reliability at the present time that it is better left out of education and practice.

I do not wish to leave the impression that some good research and worthwhile results are not available, however. Subsequent chapters will point out in detail much new and significant investigation which should be of service to all students of the behavioral aspects of chronic illness and disability. When particular caution should be exercised in the interpretation of certain studies or results, these will be stated. It is true that the "demonstration" approach, particularly in vocational rehabilitation, has been far more popular than fundamental experimental or research approach to the study of human behavior. Here again we find as the reason the overwhelming preoccupation of the rehabilitation professions with so called "practical problems," meaning their day to day concern with dealing with the problems presented by the chronically ill and disabled. It has now become abundantly clear, even to those who resist "research," that more critical and precise studies are necessary if the generation of answers is to catch up with the generation of questions.

We will first proceed to an examination of the studies of attitudes, the attitudes of important groups toward the disabled. Several of the theories reviewed have held this area to be a crucial one.

References

Adler, A. *The Practice and Theory of Individual Psychology.* 1927, Harcourt-Brace, New York.

Barker, R., Wright, B. and Gonick, M.. *Adjustment to Physical Handicaps and Illness: A Survey of the Social Psychology of Physique and Disability.* 1946, Soc. Sci. Res. Council, New York.

Parsons, T. Definitions of health and illness in the light of American values and social structure. *Patients, Physicians, and Illness.* (Jaco, Ed.) 1958, Chap. 20, pp. 165-87.

Schilder, P. *The Image and Appearance of the Human Body.* 1950, Wiley, New York.

Wright, B. *Physical Disability: A Psychological Approach.* 1960, Harper, New York.

Wright, E. The period of mourning in chronic illness. In *Medical and Psychological Teamwork in the Care of the Chronically Ill.* (Harrower, Ed.) 1955, Thomas, Springfield, Ill.

Chapter II

ATTITUDES AND DISABILITY

ONE OF THE more important subjects for study in the relationship between psychological variables and physical disability is that of attitudes. This chapter will deal exclusively with the attitudes shown the physically disabled by the non-disabled, by their families, by employers, and by the professionals who treat them and the variables which seem to account for these attitudes. Attitudes which are shown by the disabled themselves are better considered in later chapters.

There are two not necessarily opposing approaches which might account for the attitudes of others towards the physically disabled. These are the "prejudice" or "minority" and the "body-concept" views, both of which have some supporting research and evidence. It is impossible to say with complete confidence at this point which approach is most accurate and satisfactory from the standpoint of the ultimate criterion of psychology: the reliable prediction of human reactions to a given set of circumstances or stimuli. Therefore, we must assess carefully the available evidence and draw what conclusions are possible within the limitations of the data. Some preliminary conclusions will no doubt suggest themselves, but the student is cautioned against being influenced by sheer volume of expression of a particular point of view.

The study of attitudes toward the disabled has been aided recently by the development of a scale for their measurement by Yuker, Block, and Campbell (1960). The Attitudes Toward Disabled Persons (ATDP) scale is still in the process of being standardized and refined (Siller & Chipman, 1964; Yuker, Block, & Young, 1966), but has been used to apparent advantage in several studies to be reviewed here. Whether or not the ATDP scale turns out to be the valid measure of attitudes that it is hoped to be, it will have served the very important purpose of stimulating the development of objective techniques of study and measurement in a field which has been very backward in this respect.

THE BASES OF ATTITUDES
TOWARD THE DISABLED

The prejudice approach to the study of attitudes toward the disabled may be expressed as the view that the typical attitudes held by the physically normal toward the disabled is that of a negative prejudgment concerning their personal traits, including what has been called "devaluation" by Wright (1960).

Wright is one of those who would compare the attitudes shown towards the disabled with those shown toward many ethnic and religious minorities, including a stereotype of the group. Among the earlier studies referred to by Wright in support of this position is one by Ray (p. 51) in which high school students were asked to assign personality characteristics to photographs of six boys, one of whom was pictured in a wheelchair. For half the subjects, however, the same picture was presented with the wheelchair blocked out of the photograph. The result was that, "When depicted as crippled as compared to able-bodied, the stimulus was judged to be more conscientious, to feel more inferior, to be a better friend, to get better grades, to be more even-tempered, to be a better class president, to be more religious, to like parties less, and to be more unhappy" (pp. 51-2). Other studies reviewed at that time indicated only that the publicly expressed attitudes of people toward the disabled ranged from indifferent to slightly favorable. In general, Wright was not able to muster very convincing evidence from these early, and often somewhat unreliable, investigations for the notion that the disabled do in fact represent a minority group in the sense of being confined to inferior status and subject to prejudice from the majority. Now, however, there is additional evidence on the question. Yuker is another researcher who believes that prejudices toward the disabled tend to parallel prejudices toward other minority groups. His work with the ATDP scale has led him to conclude, "In many respects prejudices toward the disabled are similar to prejudices toward other groups. Thus the person who is prejudiced toward the disabled will believe that all disabled persons are alike" (Yuker, 1965, p. 16).

Initial work with the ATDP showed that scores tended to be highly correlated with the degree of contact between subjects and disabled persons. Furthermore, attitudes could be changed as a result of increased favorable interaction with disabled persons. Women tended to have a more positive attitude than men (Yuker, Block, & Campbell, 1960).

Chesler (1965) has followed with a study designed to test the idea that persons who express ethnocentric attitudes toward any "out group" will tend to express the same attitude toward other "out groups", including physically disabled persons. An Intergroup Relations Scale was employed to measure ethnocentrism in regard to attitudes toward racial, nationality, religious and social class groups. The ATDP was also given to groups of university students and high school students attending an intergroup relations conference. It was recognized that the high school group was thus atypical of adolescents and more like the university group. Their scores, in fact, did not differ significantly on either scale. All four dimensions of ethnocentrism were positively correlated, and high ethnocentrism was significantly related to lack of acceptance of the disabled. These findings would seem to support rather convincingly the point of view which relates attitudes toward the disabled with prejudice towards minorities in general, and is based on the supposition that, "Attitudes toward various minority groups tend to be organized into a coherent pattern and then expressed in a mutually supportive and consistent manner" (Chesler, p. 877). At least this interpretation would seem to be true of college students. There are other variables involved, however, as will be seen in other studies.

Another recent study done along similar lines has provided less conclusive findings. Genskow and Maglione (1965) have attempted to relate familiarity with disability and dogmatism with the expressed attitudes of college students toward the disabled. An interesting variation was introduced in having questionnaires administered to each group once by an "able-bodied" person and once by a person in a wheelchair. Subjects for this study were 111 college students in four classes at two state universities, one of which had an active and extensive handicapped student program and the other none. By the nature of the college programs, it was felt that the "familiar" and "unfamiliar" dichotomy was met, although actual contact between the subjects on either campus with the disabled was, of course, uncertain. Dogmatism, which would be characterized by intolerant, authoritarian behavior, was measured by means of Rokeach Dogmatism Scale, and the ATDP was administered for attitudes toward disability. Once again it was found that familiarity with the physically disabled leads to a more positive attitude. Differences between familiar and unfamiliar groups on the ATDP were not significant when the scale was administered by an "able-bodied" examiner, but were highly significant when given by an administrator in a wheelchair who was, in fact, not disabled. The overall influence of having an able-bodied or wheelchair-bound examiner upon attitudes was not appreciable. Neither was there found to be any significant correlation between "dogmatism" and attitudes toward the disabled. Although dogmatism and ethnocentrism would appear to be related traits, the two do not seem to bear the same relationship to attitudes toward the physically disabled as measured by the ATDP. One must apparently be intolerant and rigid specifically regarding "out groups" before this can be related to attitudes toward the disabled. Those relationships are still by no means clear, although pointing to the conclusion that familiarity with disability and ethnocentrism are important determinants of the attitudes with which we are concerned.

Lukoff and Whiteman (1964) have summarized a number of their attitude studies, most of which have been related to the attitudes of the sighted toward blindness and the blind as a group, and have concluded in general,

> There is a surprising lack of uniformity in the attitudes people have toward blind persons and blindness. We have already observed that the distinct attitudes are independent of each other. A corollary of this is that for any particular attitude for example, assessments of the potential competence of blind persons—people range from low to high, with most people somewhere in the middle, avoiding extreme in their judgements. Over the several populations studied the expected patterning of opinions did not materialize. Contrary to much of the literature, people's attitudes are not crystallized around a congery of negative images of blind people; although this may still be true for some portion of people and even in some selected environments (p. 4).

Using their own attitude scale, Lukoff and Whiteman have found a certain degree of consistency in that strong majorities of their subjects apparently perceive the blind as being more sensitive to the suffering of others, being able to lead useful lives, more appreciative of literature and music, and as having sharpened remaining senses. Contrary to the usual study which employs college students, Lukoff and Whiteman have included samples of lower and middle income households finding that, in general, a more positive attitude toward blindness was associated with an orientation toward persons, high ethnic tolerance, and low authoritarianism. An overriding general conclusion that these investigators have reached in their studies is that, "Thus the sighted respondent who expressed greater tolerance towards minority groups in general is the one who tends to express a more positive view of blind people and a greater readiness to interact with them" (p. 6). Studies by the same authors concerning the likelihood of attitude change have indicated that in high school students at least, various attitude components, e.g., pity-sympathy, protectiveness, or personal interaction, are largely independent and that some components are subject to change. Simple, factual messages were as effective in changing attitudes as the more emotional appeals with which we are all familiar.

A more recent report by Whiteman and Lukoff (1965) has implicated more subtle variations in attitude. Using social work students as subjects, it was found that blindness was evaluated as being more serious and anxiety provoking than other physical handicaps. Furthermore, there was a rather clear distinction in attitudes toward "blindness" and toward "blind persons," the condition of blindness being evaluated much more negatively than blind persons. Finally, this report points out that the subject's evaluation of blindness was far more severe than that of physical handicap in general, but there was no apparent difference in evaluations of blind and physically handicapped persons.

Certain points appear to be emerging, even at this early stage, in which our knowledge of attitudes toward the disabled is still rather primitive. First of all, there does not appear to be a universal stereotype of the "physically disabled person," and they are not all seen to be alike as Wright (1960) and

Yuker (1965) have suggested. Furthermore, based primarily on the work of Lukoff and Whiteman (1964) and Whiteman and Lukoff (1965) negative attitudes and evaluations may be more related to the *condition of disability* per se. As Wright (1960, 1964) points out, however, there is good reason to believe that a negative evaluation of the condition of disability spreads to affect the evaluation of other non-impaired characteristics of the person possessing the disability. Finally, although familiarity and ethnocentrism seem to be rather strongly related to the attitudes held toward the disabled, there is little uniformity among groups of persons except that they prefer to avoid making extreme judgments. Since much of the research in this area is done with college students, whose attitudes are quite likely to be in many instances radically different from those of the general population, generalization of the conclusions concerning attitudes cannot legitimately be carried very far at this time.

Bearing on the distinction between attitudes toward disability itself and those towards disabled persons, Barker (1964) has performed some statistical manipulations on data gathered by another investigation (Nunnally, 1961) and has found that the public conceptions of some twenty types of physical and mental conditions fall rather distinctly into "organic" and "functional" categories. The following is a summary of the major points of this article concerning the correlation of several conditions with those rated most similar to them, the primary traits associated with these conditions by the subjects, and their relative weights in the "organic-functional" dichotomy (Barker, 1964).

Subjects had rated disability categories by means of sixteen bipolar adjectives with the semantic differential technique. Intercorrelations were based on this data, and it is a good case in point that statistical manipulations do not always yield logically useful information. It is difficult to understand how the general

TABLE 1

CONCEPTS OF DISABILITIES

Condition	Rated Most Like	Rated Traits	Factor Loadings	
			Organic	Functional
Alcoholic	Neurotic	Tense, unpredictable	−0.01	0.86
Congenital* blind	Person with broken leg	Sincere, intelligent	0.90	0.31
Leprosy	Tuberculosis	Delicate, passive	0.97	0.06
Malaria	Lung cancer	Delicate, intelligent	0.90	0.31
Cancer	Malaria	Sick, delicate	0.93	0.19
Tuberculosis	Leprosy	Weak, sick	0.95	0.14

* Correlates strongly also with traumatic blindness, cancer, and other serious chronic conditions.

public, if indeed the original sample was truly representative, could in any way conceive of congenital blindness as approximated by having a broken leg. This correlation, furthermore, is completely out of phase with the other correlates which were all severe chronic conditions. All that can be concluded from this information is that the subjects chose to rate certain conditions in a similar manner on the scales provided them, and they tended to distinguish between "organic" or physical disabilities and "functional" or psychological disabilities.

Something more than the casual mention already given regarding the important variables of age and maturity and sex as determinants of attitudes is necessary. Several studies (Yuker, Block & Campbell, 1960; Chesler, 1965; Siller, 1963) have reported, using the ATDP, that women tend to show a more positive attitude and acceptance of the physically disabled than do men. A possible explanation for this has been offered by Siller who suggests, "An implication may be that the underlying feelings are similar but that women are more subject to social pressures to compensate for this attitude" (p. 14).

The variable of age has not been rigorously investigated in its relation to attitudes toward the disabled, but studies using college students and high school students usually have found a less accepting attitude among adolescents. Siller (1963) has reported samples of college, high school, and junior high students finding that college students were consistently more accepting in their attitude toward the disabled than were high school and junior high students who were quite similar. Horowitz, Rees and Horowitz (1965) have explored the attitudes and information about deafness among sixth grade, high school, college, and graduate students and a sample of PTA members. They reported that as a general trend a continuum exists with respect to age, education and maturity, and realistic attitudes and information relative to the personal and achievement characteristics of the deaf. There was no significant difference, however, among these five groups concerning their attitudes toward and ideas about the treatment or training of the deaf.

The thought is often expressed, too, that there are social class differences in attitudes toward physical disability. Lukoff and Whiteman's (1964) samples of lower and middle income households were not interpreted to have essentially different attitudes from any of their other samples. Other research of the relationship between social class and attitudes toward disability has been recently reported by Dow (1965). It was hypothesized that due to a relative emphasis attached to physique, varying inversely with social class, reactions to physical disability would be more severe at lower socioeconomic levels. No difference was found, however, between a sample of middle and lower class families.

The factors of visibility, cosmetic and functional characteristics of various disabling conditions are also frequently mentioned as a determinant of attitudes. Siller (1963) has reported that in his attitude and social distance studies those disabilities having the least cosmetic and function implications were also those reacted to most favorably by the majority of his subjects. These variables also have obvious implications for the study of the attitudes of the disabled themselves. Smits (1965) has recently found that although a sample of physically disabled adolescents received lower sociometric status ratings than their physically normal peers, there were no differences in status on the basis of the obviousness or severity of disability. Shontz (1964) discovered that in two studies with college students, the severity of a condition and secondarily its visibility were most important in determining how subjects felt they would react to having a variety of physical conditions.

Recent studies emphasizing the approach of "social distance" have reinforced the merit of differentiating attitudes toward disabling conditions and attitudes toward the disabled (Siller, 1963; Siller & Chipman, 1964; Rickard, *et al.,* 1963). Social distance is typically defined as the degree of willingness a person expresses to associate in varying degrees of intimacy with persons of differing backgrounds with regard to race, religion, nationality, social class, etc. This has also recently been applied to the study of attitudes toward disabled persons using special social distance scales designed to suit the purposes of the specific study. Most interestingly, Siller (1963) has reported that in his sample of high school and college students and adults only 9% indicated such total acceptance as willingness to have a handicapped person as a spouse. Siller's tentative interpretation of his data has been that, "Exclusion from a high degree of personal intimacy is accounted for more in terms of inferred dependency of the disabled, inability to care for day-to-day needs, and limits on sharing important recreational activities than in terms of personal feelings of aversion. Fear of social stigmata which might be attached to associating oneself with a handicapped person also receives frequent mention" (p. 15).

To summarize briefly, the "prejudice" view of attitudes toward the disabled, stating that the disabled are subject to prejudice along with other minorities and are assigned inferior status, is an oversimplification. While in general, the credibility of this viewpoint is partially supported by the limited research available at present, there are clear indications of some more subtle considerations, important variables that should not be overlooked. The reader must keep in mind also that several of the studies supporting this view are based upon restricted samples with attitudes measured by devices for which standardization is not yet complete.

The relevant information and most reasonable conclusions thus far uncovered by the researchers attempting to define the variables of "prejudice" toward the disabled are that (1) there is no universal stereotype of the physically disabled, (2) ethnocentric attitudes extend to include the physically disabled, and (3) the degree of acceptance or positive attitudes toward the disabled varies with sex, age and maturity, and possibly with level of education and sophistication as well. It is necessary to remember, too, that prejudgments concerning the attributes of the disabled are not exclusively negative as pointed out by Wright (1960, 1964). It seems common that people exaggerate positive qualities in the same way as negative ones. This phenomenon is perhaps even more difficult to explain than negative prejudgment, but Wright's (1964) explanation is as follows: "It is proposed that, although it is cognitively easier to integrate like-sign personal attributes, there are certain non-rational predispositions toward grouping traits of opposing sign. We do not feel comfortable for long with a person who is either all good or all bad" (Wright, p. 204).

As ludicrous as it may seem, we become aware of a strange belief manifest by many persons in American society that suffering and misfortune somehow make one a better man. It mysteriously develops untapped assets and results in a depth of understanding and sensitivity previously unattainable. This is a popular myth, but one apparently found even among rehabilitation professionals occasionally. I have never witnessed a person so transformed as a result of a serious permanent handicap. Segments of the health-welfare services community are notorious for the belief that a person who has never in his history been able to take advantage of the opportunities afforded by our society should, simply because he now has a disability, be expected to benefit by increased dosages of assistance.

The current evidence provides some basis for a logical separation of general attitudes toward physical impairments and disabilities on one hand and attitudes toward disabled persons on the other. Disabling conditions are seen as more inherently undesirable than are the persons who may display them. People may be perfectly willing to associate themselves with a person and accept him on the basis of personal merit, but nevertheless find the disease or injury he has suffered an event definitely to be avoided. I do not find it inconceivable, as Wright (1960) apparently does, that attitudes toward physical disability and towards disabled persons can be distinguished just the same as most people deplore poverty as a condition, or alcoholism, or homosexuality but do not necessarily have the same attitude toward their "victims." The point is that while the two sources of attitudes may be correlated, they are not inseparable and do not need to be studied as instances of the same process.

Perhaps the discussion to follow concerning the "body-concept" approach will clarify this interpretation. This approach is not as popular nor as well investigated but is promising in many respects. In terms of rationale, it will be seen that the body-concept approach is at least equally well-grounded as the "prejudice" notion.

Siller (1963), having made several studies relating personality characteristics to attitudes toward disability, has reached the general conclusion that, "The totality of data gives a slight but general confirmation of the idea that a positive self-image and stable object (interpersonal) relationships are related to acceptance of the disabled" (p. 13). In addition, Yuker, Block and Young (1966) have concluded from their own and the work of other researchers that there is substantial evidence of the relationship between the self-concept of the perceiver and attitudes manifest towards disabled persons. These authors state, "The evidence suggests the hypothesis that persons who feel confident, positive, and secure in their conception of themselves in relation to others will tend to be more positive and accepting in their attitudes toward disabled persons" (p. 65). There seems to be considerable justification, then, for the hypothesis that the way a person perceives himself, including his own physical characteristics, conditions his attitudes toward disabled persons. If we can accept conditionally such a prospect, then there is some objective evidence to allow us to evaluate this point of view.

An investigation into the relationship between the body-image of the perceiver and his attitudes toward the physically disabled has been reported by Epstein and Shontz (1962). Their objective was to determine, " whether a significant relationship exists between the attitude a non-disabled person has toward his own body and the attitudes he holds with respect to persons with physical disabilities" (p. 196). Subjects for their study were college students who were given scales designed by Secord and Jourard (1953) to measure the degree of personal satisfaction or dissatisfaction with their body and an "Attitudes Toward Persons with Disabilities" test. A general trend was found which related high "body-cathexis" scores (more satisfied body evaluation) with a more positive acceptance of the physically disabled. The authors concluded, "The findings in this investigation almost consistently support a relationship of low body-satisfaction and avoidance or rejection of the physically disabled person, of high body-satisfaction and approach or acceptance of the disabled person" (p. 200). Further research by the same authors with modifications of their measuring devices failed to support the original findings.

The "almost" consistency and inability to replicate their findings leave us entirely uncertain of the nature of the relationship, if any, between an individual's self-perception and satisfaction with his own body and his attitudes toward disabled persons. Secord and Jourard, however, have made available an apparently reliable measuring device which could profitably be employed by investigators in this area. The rationale underlying the body-cathexis/self-cathexis (BC-SC) scale is that attitudes toward the body are a reflection of attitudes toward the self, and that negative feelings (body-dissatisfaction) are associated with autistic concern with pain, disease, or injury. In their original work with this scale, Secord & Jourard found that women may be more likely to develop anxiety in relation to bodily processes than men. If this is correct, it does not agree with studies which have indicated the attitudes of women toward the disabled to be more positive than those expressed by men (Yuker, Block & Campbell, 1960; Chesler, 1965; Siller, 1963).

The body conception approach to the study of attitudes toward the physically disabled has received additional support from an investigation by Cormack (1967). The study proposed that an individual's personal body cognition, or body imagery, determines his attitudes toward disabled persons. Specifically, in terms of the cognitive dissonance methodology employed in the research, the author hypothesizes that, "The body image may be viewed in terms of two cognitive configurations (i.e., the body as it actually is, and the body as it ideally should be); the discrepancy or dissonance between the two being taken as an index of psychological discomfort in relation to the body image. On the basis of this model, it is hypothesized that those individuals who experience minimal discomfort in relation to their bodies will express more positive attitudes towards the visibly disabled than those who experience extreme discomfort" (p. 107). The results of this investigation, obtained with 318 male and female college students as subjects, supported this hypothesis based on actual vs. ideal body ratings and an "attitudes towards cripples" scale.

Some enlightening information concerning the relative attitudes of men and women toward their own bodies has been provided by Weinstein, Vetter and Sersen (1964). As a basis for their studies in relation to amputation and phantom sensations, these researchers studied 2031 physically normal men and women from high to low socioeconomic status, ranging in age from 16 to 97 years. No important differences were found in the values attached to various bodily parts between those of urban and rural background or varied economic status. This contradicts speculation by many that there are real differences in the way physique is viewed among socioeconomic groups. Subjects had been asked to rank bodily parts according to the degree they would be missed if removed. The results were presented in terms of mean rankings for men and women according to age-decade groupings (Weinstein *et al.*, p. 56) and show distinct age and sex differences in the value attached to various parts. These data are summarized in Table 2 for three of the author's age groups of each sex. We should note that as the authors point out, "It can be seen that the relatively unimportant parts, i.e., tooth, hallux, and thumb, remain very consistent over the years, while for the other parts more variability is apparent. The consistent changes which are most apparent are the devaluations, with age, of the sex-specific parts for both sexes. The other changes and fluctuations with age for parts such as ear and leg, etc., may depend upon changes in cosmetic or functional values for these parts" (p. 57). If, as Weinstein, *et al.* have indicated, there are very definite age and sex differences in bodily concepts, this may well prove to be the source of differences in attitudes expressed toward the disabled. These variables, and the others mentioned in this section as determinants of attitudes, need a great deal of further clarification.

TABLE 2

RANK-ORDER BODY PART PREFERENCES[1]

	MEN				WOMEN		
Part	20	40-49	60-69	Part	20	40-49	60-69
penis	13	13	11	tongue	12	12	12
testes	12	10	8	nose	11	8	10
tongue	11	12	13	leg	10	11	9
leg	10	7	10	eye	9	10	11
eye	9	11	12	arm	8	9	8
nose	8	8	6	foot	7	6	6
arm	7	9	9	hand	6	7	7
foot	6	5	5	ear	5	5	5
hand	5	6	7	breast	4	4	4
ear	4	4	4	thumb	3	3	3
thumb	3	3	3	hallux	2	2	2
hallux	2	2	2	tooth	1	1	1
tooth	1	1	1				

[1] from Weinstein, Vetter & Sersen, 1964, fig. 24, p. 56.

In spite of the fact that we presently have little evidence upon which to draw firm conclusions with regard to the study of attitudes, several important advances have been made. The first is, of course, the development of adequate means of measurement of attitudes relevant to disability which is not yet a reality, but promising efforts are being made in this direction. Secondly, we are now able to pinpoint more precisely what variables accounting for attitudes toward the disabled will be likely to produce significant information if thoroughly researched.

ATTITUDES OF EMPLOYERS

The attitudes of potential employers is also of vital concern to rehabilitation and particularly, of course, vocational rehabilitation. The vocational guidance and placement of the physically disabled is a difficult and demanding occupation at best, and every rehabilitation counselor is well accustomed to dealing, successfully or unsuccessfully, with the attitudes and policies of employers. Like the attitudes of the general public, they are sometimes positive, sometimes negative, but usually more or less indifferent. In this case, however, both the disabled and the rehabilitation counselor must come realistically to grips with the attitudes with which they are presented in order to attain the very basic need of economic security and independence.

Therefore, we should wish to know more about the attitudes of employers as a group who are primarily motivated by economic competition rather than social welfare, although some individuals may be strongly motivated by both forces. Much recent interest has been shown in research in this area of study because of the immediate practical value of this information.

A helpful study has been reported by Rickard, Triandis and Patterson (1963) in which samples of personnel directors and school administrators were asked to make judgments as to whether they would recommend hiring or not hiring several classes of disabled persons as an accountant or third-grade teacher. Judgments were based on four dimensions: disability (deaf, confined to wheelchair, epileptic, former psychiatric patient, ex-prisoner, tuberculosis patient and non-disabled), sex, competence and sociability. A scale was devised to measure the degree of prejudice shown, the rank ordering shown in Table 3.

TABLE 3

RANK ORDER OF DISABILITY CLASS BY
DEGREE OF PREJUDICE AGAINST

Personnel Directors (18) (as accountant)	School (as accountant)	Administrators (87) (as teachers)
epileptic	ex-prisoner	epileptic
ex-prisoner	epileptic	deaf
psychiatric	psychiatric	ex-prisoner
deaf	deaf	psychiatric
wheelchair	wheelchair	wheelchair
tuberculosis	tuberculosis	tuberculosis
non-disabled	non-disabled	non-disabled

from Rickard, Triandis & Patterson, 1963, p. 53.

Difference in degree of prejudice indicated was significantly greater for the disabled in every instance except that personnel directors did not distinguish between the person "discharged from a tuberculosis sanatorium" and a non-disabled person applying for employment. Greatest prejudice was shown toward the epileptic, ex-prisoner, and former psychiatric patient; and relatively greater prejudice was shown all disability classes when represented as applicants for employment as a teacher. In this investigation, sex was not found to be influential in determining the degree of prejudice shown except in the case of ex-prisoners and ex-mental patients where greater prejudice was shown all females. The degrees of competence and sociability were both found to be significantly related to the hiring decision. We may conclude from this, and other similar studies, that employers do tend to discriminate against the disabled applicant, but his decision can be tempered somewhat by the competence and sociability which the applicant presents.

Additional details and probable bases for this discriminatory attitude on the part of employers are contributed by a survey of firms in New York City done by the Federation Employment and Guidance Service (1959). The personnel officers of firms hiring 200 or more employees in seven types of light industry were interviewed in a 40% stratified sample and questioned specifically about their experience and hiring practices for the disability classes of cardiac, orthopedic, epileptic, cerebral palsied, and visually impaired.

By far the greatest experience of firms in this sample was with the orthopedically disabled, and next were cardiacs. In the apparel industries contacted, for example, the percentages of firms reporting experience with disabled employees were orthopedic 88%, cardiac 72%, epileptic 44%, visual impairment 12%, and cerebral palsy 6%. In the same industry, the percentages of firms excluding applicants from employment were: visual 93%, epilepsy 81%, cerebral palsy 69%, cardiac 41%, and orthopedic 10%. This study reports, "In summary, the pattern of replies for each industry clearly indicates that orthopedics are the least unacceptable of the five types of disabled included in this survey. This group is closely followed by cardiacs. The remaining three types of disabilities are clearly much more unacceptable" (FEGS, 1959, p. 27).

In this survey, which is among the best such studies available in terms of methodology and reporting, the most significant factors found to be related to willingness to hire physically disabled applicants were (1) size of the firm, (2) past experience with the disabled, (3) the type of disability, and (4) the type of business. Specifically, the larger size firms, in this study those hiring 500 or more persons, were found more favorable in their hiring practices as were those businesses engaged in wholesale and retail trades. Past experience with disabled employees indicated more favorable current attitudes, which relates to the factor of familiarity in the non-disabled as a determinant of acceptance of the disabled. The apparent preference of employers in this sample for orthopedic and cardiac disabled over those having more obvious functional limitations also corresponds to general public attitudes by which highly visible functional disabilities are reacted to more negatively (Siller, 1963; Shontz, 1964).

More surveys of employer's attitudes, policies and hiring practices have probably been accomplished specifically regarding the employment of cardiacs than any other single physical disability category. Six studies in different large metropolitan areas are summarized very briefly in Table 4 (Reeder, 1965; Olshansky, *et al,* 1955; Polner, 1958; Lee, *et al,* 1957; Reeder, 1958; and Federation Employment and Guidance Service, 1959). All of these surveys, if we can generalize, substantiate that the important factors determining employer attitudes are the size of the firm and type of business, as well as its past experience with disabled employees.

As pointed out previously, however, there are certain characteristics of disability and behavior of the applicant which have a considerable influence as well. These seem to be the obviousness and severity of the functional limitations of the disability, the applicant's competence and his degree of sociability. In these terms, it seems safe to conclude that employers as a group probably do not differ much in their basic attitudes toward physical disability and toward disabled persons from the general public.

One question which definitely needs research in this connection is the effects of the numerous requests, inquiries, and contacts made with employers by the various agencies and institutions desiring to place disabled workers with them. Do such contacts, particularly by many different groups seeking the same end—jobs, increase employment opportunities and improve employer's attitudes, or do they lead to alienation? We have all heard employers react especially negatively to being beseiged by such contacts, but even more negatively to lack of follow-up and assistance by agencies with applicants whom they actually accept for employment. Much additional valuable research could be done on the applied problems of employer attitudes and the placement of physically disabled workers. The lack of information in this area is primarily the result of the difficulty of research and lack of attractiveness of these problems to investigators.

TABLE 4 — STUDIES OF EMPLOYER PRACTICES & POLICIES CONCERNING CARDIAC WORKERS

Area (Authors)	Sample Size	Method of Sampling	% Who Had Hired	% Reported Willing	% Experienced with Cardiacs	% With Formal Policy (yes or no)	Factors found significantly related to willingness to hire cardiacs	Reasons given for not hiring
Los Angeles Co. (Reeder, 1965)	144	Stratified Random	11% (previous 2 yrs.)	47%	50%	13%	Large size; low proportion of males employed at heavy manual labor; no formal policy; wholesale or retail trades; no age limits for hiring; retaining employees developing cardiac disease.	Employee versatility Workmen's Comp. Benefit costs Jobs res. for old employees One or more of these
Boston (Olshansky, et al, 1955)	100	Selected as potential employers (mailed)	20% (previous 6 mos.)	51% (not excluding)	84%	25%	No formal policy or pre-employment physical exam; availability of suitable jobs.	Workmen's Comp. No suitable jobs Benefit costs Productivity & absenteeism
Chicago (Polner, 1958)	18	Selected med. depts. (mailed)	Not given	Not given	Not "extensive"	Not given	Not reported	Hazard to others Benefit costs Workmen's Comp.
National (Lee, et al. 1957)	19	Selected med. depts. (mailed)	42% (previous year)	Not given	All	9 yes 7 no	Not reported	Workmen's Comp. Benefit costs Not suitable jobs
Minn.-St. Paul (Reeder, 1958)	100	Stratified Random & 10 select (interview)	22%	64%	40%	50%	Attitudes toward hiring disabled in general; no age limits; lack of formal policy.	Workmen's Comp. Benefit costs Productivity
New York City (FEGS, 1959)	436	Stratified (interview)	30%	Not given	75%.	0-25% with type of industry	Experience with disabled; type and size of business—larger more favorable, wholesale & retail trades more favorable.	Workmen's Comp. Benefit costs Absenteeism Productivity

Even closer to home for most rehabilitation professions are the attitudes expressed by another group, the patient's or client's family. Attention is now directed to these questions since many professionals feel that family attitudes are those which ultimately spell success or failure in rehabilitation programs.

FAMILY ATTITUDES AND RELATIONSHIPS

Family attitudes and relationships are basically a sociological problem, and virtually all rehabilitation workers recognize their significance in carrying out rehabilitation efforts. An indication of the degree of family disruption that occurs as a result of disability is provided by Marra and Novis (1959) in a study of 52 disabled husbands and fathers. The subjects perceived the principal changes in their family relationships to be, in order of importance, (1) their wives had to assume greater responsibility for home management, (2) social and recreational activities were reduced, (3) children assumed more household duties, (4) going into debt, (5) changed plans for a larger family, (6) necessity of wife's employment, (7) increased marital discord, (8) changed plans for the children's education, and (9) changed living accommodations. From the disabled male's point of view, at least, there is considerable upheaval in family relationships as a result of disability. However, we are presently concerned with the attitudes of the non-disabled family members with respect to these changes.

It is generally conceded that rehabilitation and treatment efforts are conditioned to a large extent by the support the disabled persons receive from their families, and there is some evidence to support this opinion. In a study of the progress of 100 orthopedically disabled patients in a large rehabilitation center, Litman (1962, 1966) has reported no appreciable relationship between the degree of family *solidarity* and rehabilitation response. However, family support in terms of active interest, acceptance, and encouragement bore a definitely significant relationship to the patient's response during rehabilitation. Litman (1962, p. 253) concludes, "While the family may promote the patient's rehabilitative response through continuous supportive interest, the ultimate aims of the therapeutic staff may be gravely disturbed when the family fails to provide an atmosphere of warmth, acceptance, and encouragement, or is unwilling to accept either the performance or limitation of the disability." Another interesting finding of Litman's study was that the threat to economic security of the family did not seem to bear an important relationship to the patient's performance in his treatment program.

There is an impression on the part of many rehabilitation workers that the disabled person's role or status within the family has something to do with the family's attitudes toward and acceptance of his disability. Certainly we would expect this to differ for a child or an adult, for example. Deutsch and Goldston (1961) studied 39 patients and their families in an investigation designed to determine the relationship of family attitudes and willingness of the family to provide home care for the patient. The subjects were severely disabled polio patients who required extensive care, and it was found that the patient's position in the family was important in determining which patients would return to the home and which would be left to the care of the rehabilitation center. The disabled child was the most likely to go home as were women, both married and unmarried, and adolescent girls. Both married and unmarried men and adolescent boys were less likely to receive home care. There were, however, too few patients in these various subgroups to allow a completely reliable conclusion to be drawn based on family role.

Deutsch and Goldston (1961) also made a study of the attitudes of the family members of their group of patients, finding that those preferring to leave the care of the patient to the hospital were more unrealistic in that they tended to minimize the disabling effects and placed a higher value on the ability for voluntary movement. Expectations of the family for future improvement seemed strongly related to willingness to provide home care.

Ezra (1961), in a follow-up study of 50 men having had myocardial infarctions and their families, located an interesting discrepancy between the interpretations of family difficulties by husbands and wives. The most frequently mentioned problems related in interviews with the husbands were (1) financial problems, (2) depression, (3) curtailment of activities, and (4) fear of recurrent attack, respectively. However, the wives responded that (1) stress and tension as a result of their husbands' illness (2) financial problems, and (3) the adjustment of their husbands were more critical concerns. The wives of these disabled men interpreted their husbands as having much more serious problems of adjustment than they would admit, and a high percentage of the wives believed that the family members could have benefited from psychiatric or counseling services. Each respondent was also asked how he felt about the way the responsibilities in the home were handled in comparison to the situation that existed previous to the disability. A complex relationship between financial and economic stress and role and relationship changes in the family was found. Negative reactions to family changes corresponded with the degree of financial difficulty in which the family was placed.

In addition to the few studies just quoted concerning the attitudes of the family and the influences on the behavior of the disabled member, a number of sociological investigations have been made into the response of the family itself to the crisis of illness or disability. These are interesting studies and deserve a great deal more investigation, especially as the families' behavior affects that of our patients and clients. Presently, however, the indications are that family solidarity and similar descriptions have little to do with the patient's therapeutic performance or motivation (Litman, 1962, 1966).

A logical explanation for this apparent paradox has been offered by Litman who has concluded, "To some extent, such findings are perhaps a function of the very nature of the treatment program itself. That is, during the particular phase of rehabilitation studied, the family must more or less relinquish all responsibility for the care and treatment of their loved one" (1966, p. 214). This brings up another important source of attitudes, those of the professionals responsible for the individual's care and rehabilitation.

ATTITUDES OF STAFF AND PROFESSIONALS

The attitudes of professionals in rehabilitation toward their patients or clients have not been subjected to sufficient investigation, experimental or administrative. Yet those attitudes are probably more important in determining the individual's response to treatment and rehabilitation planning than any other single force. Unfortunately, professionals in health and rehabilitation fields are typically trained only to perform certain technical duties and have little attention called to the subtleties of the situations in which they work, which may, in fact, markedly influence those aspects of the patient's behavior they wish to modify. The hospital or rehabilitation center is an exceedingly peculiar environment that any patient finds himself hard pressed to cope with efficiently. The standardization, impersonal nature and strangeness of this environment are inherently undesirable to most persons who must nevertheless yield virtually all control over their behavior to those in authoritiy. The attitudes that determine how this authority is exercised are therefore crucial to understanding the patient's emotional responses to the situation.

There is little doubt that the care and rehabilitation of the disabled is a complex and demanding task. Yet we should wonder, as does DuBrow (1965) if such stereotypic labels tossed about by professionals in discussing their charges, such as "CPs," "CVAs," "Quads," or "Paras" are not quite similar to the prejudgments of the general non-disabled public. DuBrow (p. 25) states, "One is prone to wonder if this kind of wastebasket labeling does not manifest a disregard for individuality, a sort of clubhouse disdain for the inferior by members of the 'pro' team." There is very little specific information regarding professional attitudes in various circumstances and settings in rehabilitation, and the effect of such attitudes as may be found upon the individual's response to rehabilitation efforts. There have, however, been techniques reported for making such investigations. Ford, Liske, and Ort (1962) have employed a sentence-completion method (p. 794) in which subjects complete such items as "Patients with chronic disease are . . ." and "When I see a patient with relentlessly progressive disease . . .," to investigate staff attitudes. Barrell, DeWolfe, and Cummings (1965) have more recently reported on the development and validation of a rating scale called the "Philosophy of Treatment Form (POT)" which measures staff attitudes in several areas.

The study of Ford *et al.,* presents some findings based upon the responses of medical faculty and students. Essentially, the reactions of both groups were found to be neutral, i.e., neither strong approach nor avoidance of chronic disease patients. However, groups clearly expressed more favorable feelings and tendencies to approach situations involving diagnosis and treatment and to have avoidance tendencies toward demanding, hostile, severely disabled, or hopelessly ill patients. On the other hand, Arnholter (1963) has reported that, using the ATDP scale, staff and professionals working with the disabled at Goodwill Industries were much more positive in their attitudes than were disabled workers themselves.

Obviously, studies of staff and professional attitudes are an important need. Schlesinger (1963 a,b) has made an analysis of several questions in this regard which hopefully will suggest further study. The presence of staff conflicts such as custodial demands versus therapeutic objectives becomes even more important as we consider present and impending staff shortages and demand for health and rehabilitation services. Considerably more knowledge is needed in all circumstances in which attitudes may influence rehabilitation efforts.

Barrell, DeWolfe and Cummings (1967) have contributed the only research to the point, in which an attempt was made to correlate the patient's emotional response to prolonged hospitalization for physical illness with staff attitudes manifest on their wards. The study was an elaborate and well-planned one involving nineteen wards of eight Veterans Administration hospitals around the country. The results of their study were surprising, and Barrell, *et al.* conclude, "The results appeared to indicate that many of our cherished beliefs about what improves patients' satisfaction with hospitalization apply primarily to patients with acute medical disorders or short hospitalizations. Based on the results of the current study, it seems possible that patients with a chronic medical disorder which requires a relatively long hospitalization prefer friendly but impersonal care and less concern about their individual needs'' (p. 258).

References

Barker, D.   Concepts of disabilities. *Pers. Guid. J.*, 1964, **43**, 371-4.

Barrell, R., De Wolfe, A. & Cummings, J.   A measure of staff attitudes toward care of physically ill patients. *J. Consult. Psychol.*, 1965, **29**, 218-22.

Barrell, R., De Wolfe, A. & Cummings, J.   Personnel attitudes and patients' emotional response to hospitalization for physical illness. *J. Psychol.*, 1967, **65**, 253-60.

Chesler, M.   Ethnocentrism and attitudes toward the physically disabled. *J. Pers. Soc. Psychol.*, 1965, **2**, 877-82.

Cormack, P.   The relationship between body cognition and attitudes expressed toward the visibly disabled. *Rehab. Couns. Bull.*, 1967, **11**, 106-09.

Deutsch, C. & Goldston, J.   Patient and family attitudes and their relationship to home placement of the severely disabled. *Rehab. Couns. Bull.*, 1961, **4**, 169-79.

Dow, T.   Social class and reaction to physical disability. *Psychol. Repts.*, 1965, **17**, 39-62.

Du Brow, A.   Attitudes toward disability. *J. Rehab.*, 1965, **31**, 25-6.

Epstein, S. & Shontz, F.   Attitudes toward persons with physical disabilities as a function of attitudes toward one's own body. *Rehab. Couns. Bull.*, 1962, **5**, 196-201.

Ezra, J.   *Social and Economic Effects on Families of Patients with Myocardial Infarctions.* 1961, University of Denver, Colorado.

Fed. Employment and Guidance Service. *Survey of Employer's Practices and Policies in the Hiring of Physically Impaired Workers.* 1951, FEGS, New York.

Ford, A., Liske, R. & Ort, R.   Reactions of physicians and medical students to chronic illness. *J. Chron. Dis.*, 1962, **15**, 785-94.

Genskow, J. & Maglione, F. Familiarity, dogmatism, and reported student attitudes toward the disabled. *J. Soc. Psychol.*, 1965, **66**, 329-41.

Horowitz, L., Rees, N. & Horowitz, M. Attitudes toward deafness as a function of increasing maturity. *J. Soc. Psychol.*, 1965, **66**, 331-6.

Lee, P., Rusk, H., White, P. & Williams, B. Cardiac rehabilitation: Questionnaire survey of medical directors in industry. *JAMA*, 1957, **165**, 787-91.

Litman, T. The influence of self-conception and life orientation factors in the rehabilitation of the orthopedically disabled. *J. Health Hum. Behav.*, 1962, **3**, 249-56.

Litman, T. The family and physical rehabilitation. *J. Chron. Dis.*, 1966, **19**, 211-17.

Lukoff, I. & Whiteman, M. Attitudes Toward Blindness. 1964, Paper presented at Amer. Fed. Cath. Wkrs. for the Blind, New York.

Marra, J. & Novis, F. Family problems in rehabilitation counseling. *Pers. Guid. J.*, 1959, **38**, 40-2.

Nunally, J. *Popular Conceptions of Mental Health.* 1961, Holt, Rinehart & Winston, New York.

Olshansky, S., Friedland, S., Clark, R. & Sprague, H. A survey of employment policies as related to cardiac patients in greater Boston. *New Eng. J. Med.*, 1955, **253**, 506-10.

Polner, W. Hiring limitations on cardiacs in Chicago area firms. *Indust. Med. & Surg.*, 1958, **27**, 316-20.

Rickard, T., Triandis, H. & Patterson, C. Indices of employer prejudice toward disabled applicants. *J. Appl. Psychol.*, 1963, **47**, 52-5.

Reeder, L. Employment practices and the cardiac. *J. Chron. Dis.*, 1965, **18**, 951-63.

Reeder, L. & Donahue, G.   Cardiac employment potential in urban society. *J. Chron. Dis.*, 1958, **8**, 230-43.

Schlesinger, L.   Staff authority and patient participation in rehabilitation. *Rehab. Lit.*, 1963 a, **24**, 247-9.

Schlesinger, L.   Staff tensions and needed skills in staff-patient interactions. *Rehab. Lit.*, 1963 b, **24**, 362-5.

Secord, P. & Jourard, S.   Appraisal of body-cathexis: Body cathexis and the self. *J. Consult. Psychol.*, 1953, **17**, 343-7.

Shontz, F.   Body-Part Size Judgement. 1964, Univ. Kan., Lawrence. Final report, VRA proj. No. 814 (mimeo).

Siller, J.   Reactions to physical disability. *Rehab. Couns. Bull.*, 1963, **7**, 12-16.

Siller, J. & Chipman, A.   Factorial structure and correlates of the attitudes toward disabled persons scale. *Educ. Psychol. Measmt.*, 1964, **24**, 831-40.

Smits, S.   The reactions of self and others to the obviousness and severity of physical disability. *Rehab. Couns. Bull.*, 1965, **9**, 41-6.

Weinstein, S., Vetter, R. & Sersen, E. Physiological and Experiential Concomitants of the Phantom. 1964, Albert Einstein Coll. Med., New York, Final report, VRA Proj. No. 427 (mimeo).

Whiteman, M. & Lukoff, I.   Attitudes toward blindness and other physical handicaps. *J. Soc. Psychol.*, 1965, **66**, 135-45.

Wright, B.   *Physical Disability: A Psychological Approach.* 1960, Harper, New York.

Wright, B.   Spread in adjustment to disability. *Bull. Men. Clin.*, 1964, **28**, 198-208.

Yuker, H.   Attitudes as determinants of behavior. *J. Rehab.*, 1965, **31**, 15-16.

Yuker, H., Block, J. & Campbell, W. *A Scale to Measure Attitudes Toward Disabled Persons.* 1960, Hum. Resources Study No. 5, Hum. Resources Res. Found., Albertson, N.Y.

Yuker, H., Block, J. & Young, J. *The Measurement of Attitudes Toward Disabled Persons.* Hum. Resources Study No. 7, 1966, Human Resources Center, Albertson, N.Y.

Chapter III

EMOTIONAL FACTORS IN ILLNESS AND DISABILITY

THE MATTER of how individuals respond and adjust to the occurrence of permanent physical damage due to disease or injury and the residual disability that often ensues is to some *the* most important aspect of rehabilitation. Indeed, it is a universal law of rehabilitation, if any of the principles by which we operate can be qualified as such, that any attempts to assist the chronically ill or disabled will be tempered by the person's emotional responses to the situation—his acceptance and adaptation to his condition. Furthermore, the success of our efforts in long-term benefits to the individual is said to depend largely upon the patient or client's personal adjustment. Therefore, it is of utmost importance that we examine carefully and critically the evidence that research has been able to uncover thus far in relation to the emotional adjustment of the physically disabled.

Contrary to a great deal of the literature on this subject, little attention will be given in these pages to the attempt to differentiate various types of physical disability on the basis of specific personality characteristics. This is intentional since the indications are that individuals within disability categories *do not* share common personality patterns as has frequently been supposed. Wright's (1960) assessment of efforts to identify distinguishing personality traits for various disability groups was that, "Somatic abnormality as a physical fact is not linked in a direct or simple way to psychological behavior . . . There is also no clear evidence of an association between types of physical disability and particular personality characteristics" (pp. 373-4). Recent reviews of the evidence for several disability groups— Moos (1964) in rheumatoid arthritis, Tizard (1962) in epilepsy, Cohen (1962), and Harrower and Kraus (1951) in multiple sclerosis, and other individual studies with other groups—have reached essentially the same conclusion. Nevertheless, virtually all writers on the subject agree that physical disability often leads to emotional problems and difficulties in personal adjustment. The two major questions chosen for this discussion, therefore, are the emotional reactions to illness and disability as a threat to personal integrity, and the influence of emotional factors upon treatment and rehabilitation. Included in this discussion will be a summary of the available evidence concerning reactions to illness, disability, and hospitalization, the defenses and attitudes manifest in the adjustment process, and emotional determinants of the degree of improvement and response to rehabilitation efforts by the patient.

EMOTIONAL REACTIONS TO ILLNESS AND DISABILITY

Before launching an examination of the research on the emotional reactions to physical disability, some consideration is due the circumstances underlying these problems. Barker, Wright and Gonick's (1946) writings on the "social psychology of acute illness" will serve as a suitable introduction. As we have seen in Parsons' (1958) social theory, with the onset of illness the individual is presumed to adopt a new role, a sick role in which he is exempted from usual demands contingent upon his recognition that his state is inherently undesirable, and that he cooperate with others in seeking help and in trying to "get well." The adjustment to new role demands is not without emotional turmoil.

From the very beginning of illness, the patient is in a state of conflict, according to Barker, *et al* (1946), the magnitude of which will depend upon his conception of the degree of attractiveness and unattractiveness of the alternatives. Very basically, the patient's symptoms and the prospect of treatments are unattractive (painful, expensive, etc.), but treatment offers possible remission and return to a healthy state. The vacillation between seeking and avoiding treatment is accompanied by emotional stress which in turn affects the responses to treatment. Entry into treatment also produces a certain amount of "negative" emotional response due to the effects of unfamiliarity, strangeness, and uncertainty in the environment and procedures employed. In this state of anxiety and arousal, the likelihood is greatly increased that the patient will be influenced by irrelevant, unreliable or even erroneous cues, misinterpreting and developing expectations that are sometimes unreasonable and lead the staff to wonder how such peculiar notions could have arisen. Barker, *et al,* suggest that familiarization of the patient with the institution, the equipment and procedures used, reduces resistance and emotional arousal. These aspects of emotional response to illness are relatively superficial, easily observed and resolved with a little thought on the part of professional personnel. However, many reactions are much more pervasive.

Barker, *et al.,* have stated that during physical illness the patient's world undergoes a great reduction in scope; the psychological world becomes egocentric. Former determinants of behavior lose their potency, and influences are restricted to only a few persons and needs. A shift of attention takes place in which internal cues are much more potent than externally located factors. The healthy person is almost totally unaware of physiological processes, but the sick are alert to even minor variations. As the patient's interests narrow, fewer stimuli exist for him, and this increased egocentricity decreases his awareness and appreciation for the needs of others. This, at least, is one conception of emotional processes during acute stages of illness (pp. 228-46).

Shontz, Fink and Hallenbeck (1960) state it another way. Their conception has been that chronic physical illness is a threat to the individual which prevents the normal completion of energy cycles, the intensity of which is determined by the amount of energy blocked from expression. In other words, under the threat of illness, the individual's energy is redistributed into channels directly concerned with physical functioning and other values are temporarily overshadowed. This conception is based on A.H. Maslow's hierarchy of needs which states that physiological and safety needs are the most fundamental, and higher order needs cannot become potent until these more basic ones have been satisfied. The hypothesis of Shontz, *et al.* for a study to test this conception was that the conditions of illness lead to an increase in energy flow to relationships that depend upon physical functions at the sacrifice of energy usually invested in other demands. "The increased investment of energy in body relationships should, therefore, be reflected in a pattern of personal values which stresses the importance of body functioning as opposed to psychosocial functioning" (p. 144). The authors requested 31 chronically ill and 42 physically normal persons to assign relative values to a total of 24 physical and psychosocial factors: such as, "sanity, ability to think, general physical health, home, education, job," etc., after controlling for the factors of age, sex and verbal intelligence. The result of the study was that their group of chronically ill individuals showed a slight trend to a " relative emphasis upon the importance of bodily things as opposed to psychosocial things, but only as a general statement applicable to the groups of subjects as a whole" (p. 145). The chronically ill group valued the use of the body from the neck down, control of bladder and ability to walk, more than the healthy group who placed greater value on education, ability to love, children, religion, and sexual capacities. On the other hand, when the responses of individual subjects were analyzed, a common value pattern was found for *all* the subjects. Shontz, *et al.* conclude, "The basic balance of personal values between psychosocial and physical factors is only slightly disturbed by chronic physical illness" (p. 146).

It may well be that constriction and egocentricity are predominant during the acute stages of illness or recovery from injury as Barker, *et al.* suppose; but there are also indications that, if illness is of a chronic nature, balance is gradually restored once the early shock, anxiety, and emotional distress have abated. Although the value system and responsiveness of the patient may stabilize in time, this does not mean that the process of adjustment is complete. Rather, it is at this point that environmental influences within the institution, hospital or rehabilitation center become critical.

One very significant environmental variable which is seldom mentioned, but which I feel is quite important, is the problem of boredom. By the term "boredom" I do not mean strictly the affective result of cognitive deprivation alone, but also the result of sensory and social isolation and restricted mobility. Heron (1966) has pointed out quite dramatically the behavioral disruption which occurs as a result of these kinds of restrictions placed upon human beings. Subjects in sensory deprivation experiments described by Heron were required to lie in bed in a lighted cubicle 24 hours a day as long as they would stay. Visual, auditory, and tactile experiences were severely restricted during this time, and a wide variety of behaviors measured. The results were truly surprising, even to the experimenters. Gross disturbances occurred in cognitive, perceptual, and motor performances as a result of environmental restriction. Subjects' reports of their experience were even more fascinating. It seemed quite clear even in the earliest experiments that as the subjects lay isolated their thought processes gradually changed, eventually reaching the point where visual, auditory, and somatic hallucinations occurred. They became quite irritable, childish, and suspicious of the experimenters. Several subjects reported peculiar sensations of touch and movement such as electric shocks, the presence of another body lying beside or overlapping their own, and general "bodily strangeness."

Heron has given the following neurophysiological explanation for these reactions:

> The recent studies indicate that normal functioning of the brain depends on a continuing arousal reaction generated in the reticular formation, which in turn depends on constant sensory bombardment. It appears that, aside from their specific functions, sensory stimuli have the general function of maintaining this arousal, and they rapidly lose their power to do so if they are restricted to the monotonously repeated stimulation of an unchanging environment (p. 86).

It would seem a reasonable hypothesis that much of the behavior and emotional disturbance observed in many different types of physical disability, particularly during prolonged hospitalization, may be due to the effects of limitations imposed upon sensory and kinesthetic experience. Indeed, this has been demonstrated to operate in parkinsonism (Ploski, Levita & Riklan, 1966; Riklan & Levita, 1966) and it may be that the peculiar sensations and emotional distress reported by persons with paraplegia, quadriplegia, amputation, or hemiparesis may be due to the same factors.

Riklan and Levita have summarized the findings of their preoperative studies with Parkinson patients as follows:

> Voluntary movement impairment, considered as one of the most direct measures of general parkinsonian incapacitation, was associated with reliable and pervasive intellectual and perceptual losses and with impoverishment of personality resources. Such results were attributed to the fact that parkinsonians with more significant voluntary movement impairment tend to be more generally bedridden or home-bound, markedly limited in their opportunity for interpersonal relationships, and largely isolated from sensory stimulation. Moreover, these pa-

tients lack the sensory-kinesthetic feedback derived from movement itself (p. 373).

These authors have reported behaviors very similar to those produced and reported by Heron (1966), their interpretation made even more plausible because of the involvement of the reticular activating system in parkinsonism.

A closely aligned type of isolation which deserves a great deal more attention is that of social isolation. Physical disabilities and chronic illness, especially when they interfere with communication and mobility, may also be expected to disrupt social participation, recreation, and interpersonal relationships to some extent. Undoubtedly, such isolation is capable of producing emotional distress as does sensory isolation, although probably adjusted to more readily and with less behavioral disorganization. The social isolation of the physically disabled has recently been subject to increased attention and action-oriented programs designed to increase opportunities and eliminate some obstacles such as "architectural barriers" to the disabled. Some communities have conducted studies and surveys and published guides for the disabled who are ambulatory, indicating all types of public facilities accessible to them. This may partially alleviate the problems of social isolation due to restricted mobility, but we still have other problems to contend with in the same area. Social isolation would not be easily overcome for those individuals who are confined to bed, home, hospitals, or other institutions for extended periods of time, and yet this constitutes a very grave source of deprivation which could certainly curtail normal patterns of human interaction.

The depressive reactions shown with impairments of the visual and auditory systems may also be explainable on the basis of sensory deprivation (Myklebust, 1964). Depressive reactions are a frequent occurrence in all types of physical disablement, particularly in the acute stages. Although this is most frequently ascribed to "mourning" the lost function or body part, it is equally likely that the depressive reactions are due to sensory deprivation and restricted environmental stimulation. It also appears that body-image distortions characteristic of a variety of disabling conditions have this basis, distortions having been produced in normals under conditions of sensory isolation (Heron).

EFFECTS OF RESTRICTED MOBILITY

The effects of restricted voluntary movement upon perceptual, affective, and cognitive changes in humans have not been sub-jected to careful controlled experiment as have other sources of sensory restriction. Freedman, Grunebaum, and Greenblatt (1961), however, suspect a critical difference in sensory depriva-tion studies due to the degree of movement allowed. They state in reviewing a number of studies that, "In every instance of restricted motility, hallucinations have been reported, while in two experimental situations with free motility, minimal or no hallucinations were reported" (p. 61).

Mendelson, *et al.* (1961) have conducted some studies prompted by their observations of hallucinations in poliomyelitis patients in respirators. They, therefore, studied the responses of twelve adult, physically normal persons in a situation of restricted sensory input and voluntary movement. Subjects were placed in a tank-type respirator but allowed to breathe for themselves. Arms and legs were encased in rigid cylinders to inhibit move-ment and tactile contact, and with the subject lying on his back he was unable to see any part of his body. Auditory and visual stimulation were restricted, but not eliminated, and no communication with the experimenter was permitted. Many variables of psychological and physiological processes were mon-itored until the subject asked to be released. Although the controlled conditions of Mendelson do not quite duplicate the situations we are most interested in at the moment, they do reflect the emotional distress prompted by sensory isolation and restricted movement. There was considerable individual variance in response to this situation, but subjects consistently reported distress and difficulty in thinking and remaining coherent. The stress reactions were corroborated by a number of continuous physiological measures.

EFFECTS OF SENSORY RESTRICTION

If the problem were to be thoroughly researched, I believe one could identify significant behavioral disturbances attributable to the sensory isolation to which the chronically ill and disabled are subjected during prolonged hospitalization and home confinement. Limited mobility and severely restricted sensory stimulation may combine to produce behavioral disruptions that can interfere with treatment and rehabilitation objectives, but are typically ascribed to very nebulous concepts such as "dependency" and "lack of motivation."

Unfortunately, it will be necessary to use extreme examples to illustrate this point. Isolation due to permanent partial or total loss of a receptor system, eliminating or seriously restricting a source of sensory input such as in deafness or blindness, has many behavioral effects. However, for the present, we shall examine only some of the more comprehensive studies concerning the problems of emotional adjustment accompanying sensory isolation. Notably, it has only been relatively recently (Axelrod, 1959; Myklebust, 1964; Sterritt, Camp & Lipman, 1966) that controlled experiments have shown us that disruption of one sensory system is accompanied by problems in information processing in remaining systems.

There is evidence, in general, that sensory loss leads to a relatively high rate of emotional maladjustment and immaturity, social immaturity and isolation, and negative attitudes with respect to social and occupational opportunities. The studies in this connection are many and varied and the debate continues as to whether the findings are in fact due to (1) sensory loss itself, (2) early experiences and education, (3) institutionalization, or (4) social acceptance. Whatever the reason, sensory loss does apparently frequently lead to difficulties in emotional adjustment; even experimental animal studies indicate that permanent changes result from early sensory isolation. The question of whether emotional problems are produced by sensory deprivation per se will probably not be settled for some time to come. However, it is useful to point out some general findings in relation to the process of emotional adjustment.

The most comprehensive investigation of adjustment to visual loss has been reported by Bauman (1954). A total of 443 individuals with visual loss from legal blindness to no useful vision were sampled in six states. The sample was stratified according to employment, sex, urban-rural residence, and race in each state. Within the sample, groups were compared who were (a) employed and generally well adjusted, (b) not employed, but generally well adjusted, (c) unemployed and poorly adjusted. Several objective criteria were used to compose the comparison groups (Bauman, p. 14-15), the proportions within the total sample finally being determined to be: Group A, 37%; Group B, 34%; and Group C, 29%.

It was determined that no difference existed between the comparison groups in reported initial reactions to visual loss, about the same proportions in each reporting feeling very disturbed emotionally. The suddenness or gradualness of onset of visual loss was not especially significant, nor was the amount of remaining vision. The insignificance of the degree of visual loss to personality adjustment has since been supported by Greenberg and Jordan (1957).

Bauman's (1954) study has also partially answered the question of the role of hope for return of sight in the emotional adjustment of the visually disabled. Less than one in five of the total sample reported any hope that their vision might be improved or restored, but those who did, contrary to many opinions, did not show a greater degree of maladjustment and were somewhat more mobile with a greater degree of useful vision. Thume and Murphree (1961) have since reported, however, in a similar proportion of persons expressing hope for return of sight, that such hopes preclude the acceptance and use of the white cane as a travel aid and limit independent travel and vocational adjustment. Bauman (1954) compared cane users, dog users, and those who used neither, finding that those who used guide dogs differed significantly from the other two groups in that they were more positive in their attitudes toward blindness, had greater social competency, and less feelings of inadequacy.

In general, the results of Bauman's study indicate the importance of emotional factors in successful adjustment to visual loss. There was a clearly progressive relationship between better general adjustment and the degree of social competency, absence of paranoid tendencies and feelings of inadequacy, and more positive attitudes toward visual loss.

By far the most complete and informative investigation of the mental health aspects of hearing loss has been contributed by Rainer, *et al.* (1963) based on samples of the deaf throughout the state of New York. A few of the major findings of the study are as follows:

1. The deaf were found to be in serious need of specialized services for genetic, family and personal counseling.

2. A study of criminal acts committed by 51 deaf persons between 1957-61 indicated a high proportion of sexual offenses and assaults. Deaf offenders were significantly more immature and impulsive than hearing offenders.

3. Among 217 deaf persons seeking outpatient psychiatric care as part of the study, the highest proportions were of schizophrenic reactions and personality trait disturbances. The symptomatology displayed was not different from the hearing with these disorders.

4. A total of 230 deaf patients in state mental hospitals were identified, showing approximately the same proportions of various disorders as the hearing population but with a higher proportion of mental deficiency accompanying psychosis. The deaf patients had longer periods of hospitalization.

It should be evident from the foregoing investigations that the disabilities of sensory loss do represent serious obstacles to satisfactory personal and emotional adjustment. Furthermore, whatever the exact cause in producing these problems, there is a definite need for specialized rehabilitation and treatment services above those required by the general population.

Although the degree of isolation imposed by sensory loss is, of course, far more extreme than the isolation occurring in hospitalization, treatment or home confinement, it should be abundantly clear that restricted sensory input is not easily accommodated by human beings. Furthermore, it is suggested that much of the emotional distress seen, especially in the acute stages of illness and disability, is due to restricted mobility and sensory isolation. There is no experimental evidence to support this point of view at present, however. Hence, the remaining discussion will focus on what objective facts there are in regard to some enlightening descriptive research on emotional response to disability.

THE SITUATIONAL STRESSES OF ILLNESS AND DISABILITY

A very fundamental need for rehabilitation professionals is to understand and predict the emotional response of those who are ill or disabled. One would think, because of the implications of the question for treatment and rehabilitation efforts, that there would be a considerable amount of discrete information to aid us. However, this has not been the case, and it has only been relatively recently that behavioral scientists became interested in the problem.

A highly informative recent contribution has been made by the investigation of DeWolfe, Barrell, and Cummings (1966) conducted with 517 male patients in ten Veterans Administration Hospitals in eight states. These researchers gathered data on many different aspects of the patients' responses to hospitalization for physical illness including patients' opinions of staff performance, hospital experiences, characteristic level of anxiety and personality and emotional adjustment factors. All of the subjects were hospitalized for physical disease for a minimum of six weeks.

A very important determinant of this sample of patients' emotional response to hospitalization was age at admission. Older patients were found to be significantly more comfortable with the hospitalization experience, which the authors interpret as possibly due to (1) fewer pressures and responsibilities or (2) older patients being better able to accept the dependent role required of them. In addition, patients' characteristic level of anxiety was found to be a significant variable. Persons with high anxiety levels showed less favorable emotional response to hospitalization.

In regard to hospital attitudes, DeWolfe, *et al.* have identified what appear to be emotional patterns which may determine the patients' responses to hospitalization. On one hand were those who preferred authoritarian control and were somewhat negative toward other patients, and on the other were those critical of staff performance and who actively sought information about their condition. The former showed less emotional discomfort to their hospitalization and were also older.

The next logical question is, what influence does the patient's emotional reactions have upon his response to treatment? DeWolfe, *et al.* are unclear on this question, but their results have indicated that in terms of physicians' ratings, at least, no significant relationship existed between emotional adjustment in the hospital and degree of recovery. Indeed, there was some suggestion, due to the influence of older patients in this sample, that less favorable prognoses for present and predicted recovery were accompanied by less emotional discomfort in the hospital. The latter finding, while seemingly inconsistent, might indicate that some degree of emotional arousal and discomfort is conducive to better recovery. This remains to be seen, but if we equate emotional discomfort and characteristic level of anxiety with general drive or arousal level, then we might expect the following relationship: either excessively high distress or arousal levels or the absence or very low levels of arousal yield poorer results in terms of patient response to treatment. A moderate degree of discomfort and arousal in the patient facilitates rehabilitation. This hypothesis has rather obvious implications for motivation in rehabilitation and will be enlarged upon in a later section.

Recent studies by Krause (1964) have utilized something of a critical incident approach to study the occurrence of emotional crises in the rehabilitation center setting. The crises observed in this study were of considerably varying nature, but an important general finding was that "The greater the number of simultaneous social transitions of an individual vis-a-vis individuals and groups to whom he closely bonded emotionally, the higher the probability of an increase in his level of anxiety and the onset of a crisis" (p. 41). Specifically, it was determined that those clients who lived at home and came to the rehabilitation center for training and treatment had crises early upon entrance to the center. Those who "lived in" at the center had crises late in their programs near the exit from the center. Evidently, then, the transitional periods of entry and termination are critical points of emotional adjustment for rehabilitation center patients. Most likely, this finding is due to the introduction of conflict and uncertainty which increases the patient's anxiety or emotional arousal to a level which inhibits satisfactory adaptation and problem resolution. It is fundamental in human behavior that people strive for consistency and stability and resist change. Any change, whether subjectively interpreted as positive or negative, requires first of all increased arousal to deal with the change. An appraisal of the changed elements of the situation and revision of concepts and behavior to accommodate and act upon the change are also necessary. Response to change then is determined primarily by the nature of the change and the number and kinds of concepts requiring modification. Novelty and change may be environmental or physical, positive or negative, they still require adaptive mechanisms, are resisted by the human organism and are accompanied by increased arousal. Consequently, rehabilitation staffs should be alert to situations of change and transition, and should be most active in providing information, support, and resources necessary for the individual's efficient adaptation. To the extent that patients' perceptions and appraisals are accurate and they possess the necessary resources for behavior modification, transition and change can be adequately met. While this conception of human response to change is admittedly oversimplified, I believe it may be found to fit a wide variety of situations that arise in rehabilitation.

RELATION OF PHYSICAL CHANGES TO EMOTIONAL BEHAVIOR

It seems relevant to mention the possible influence of an individual's physical injury upon his emotional behavior, although not a great deal of objective information is available on the matter. Even the perception of pain has been recognized in recent years to be conditioned by social and cultural factors as well as emotional arousal (Melzack, 1961). Still, not a great deal is known about the effects of permanent physical injury upon subsequent emotional behavior, particularly when the central nervous system is involved. Brain damaged persons, of course, have often been shown to display a wide array of emotional responses which arise principally from loss of inhibition and control over behavior.

A recent investigation, however, has reported upon the subjective impressions of 25 paraplegic men injured at various levels (Hohmann, 1966). They were asked to relate, in a structured interview, changes in specific "feelings" in situations of sexual excitement, fear, anger, etc., before and since their injuries. The notion that emotional changes may have resulted from spinal cord transection was suggested to the author by the theory of emotional behavior developed by Wenger (1956) who believes emotions to be the perception of visceral and striate muscle activity. Hohmann (1966) found as a result of his studies that experienced emotional feelings were significantly decreased after injury in his subjects, particularly those feelings associated with sexual excitement, anger, and fear, regardless of the level of the injury. On the other hand, his subjects reported a dramatic increase in emotional feelings of "sentimentality" following injury. Another important finding of this study indicates that even though the actual experienced emotional feeling may be greatly decreased or even absent, the display of overt behavior consistent with the emotion may continue. Hohmann states, "It seems possible that such acts represent learned reactions and are more or less devoid of feeling" (1954). Certain behaviors may persist because they are effective in getting results, not because of the intense emotion felt. Hohmann concludes, "Substantiation is offered for the belief that disruption of the ANS and its afferent return causes notable disturbances in the mental correlates of emotion" (p. 155).

Research in the vein reported by Hohmann in regard to the effects of actual physical damage upon emotional behavior could be quite valuable to rehabilitation. One would wish that researchers would show more interest in clinical investigations of this type.

Probably another important factor in determining emotional behavior is the highly subjective experience of pain. The perception of pain is obviously an event associated with physical injury which is usually accompanied by some degree of emotional arousal. Recent research (Melzack, 1961; Melzack & Wall, 1965) has contradicted the classical views of pain perception and instead has indicated that, "The psychological evidence strongly supports the view of pain as a perceptual experience whose quality and intensity are influenced by the unique past history of the individual, by the meaning he gives to the pain-producing situation and by his 'state of mind' at the moment" (Melzack, p. 49). It has been pointed out by these same workers that intense prolonged attention will diminish pain perception, but that the mere anticipation of pain raises anxiety level and hence the intensity of perceived pain. Since the perception or anticipation of pain serves to increase anxiety and emotional arousal, as well as the reverse, this surely represents an important variable in individual behavior in rehabilitation.

Melzack and Wall also point out that some sixteen different surgical procedures have been designed to alleviate pain, but with only moderate success. Even more perplexing is the phantom pain of some amputees and paraplegic persons. Weinstein, Vetter, and Sersen (1964) have reported the incidence of painful phantoms in certain groups studied to be from 24% in cases of mastectomy to over 40% in limb amputations and in paraplegia. Simmel (1959) does not believe the rate to be this high but feels phantom pain to be typically associated with severe personality disturbances.

It seems that we may be faced with a circular process. Illness and disability have the singular effect of increasing somatic preoccupation, which in turn sensitizes the individual to painful stimuli. The perception of pain may be expected to affect response to diagnostic and treatment situations and rehabilitation because the experience or anticipation of pain leads to increased emotional arousal which interferes with adaptation and learning. Since the perception of pain is such a subjective experience, we are confronted with a problem which has implications for motivation as well as emotional response to illness and disability.

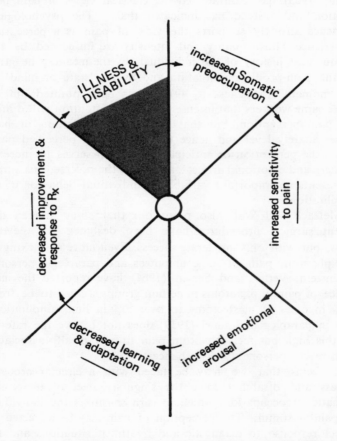

FIG. 1. Circular process of emotional arousal and illness.

The experience of pain is a most fundamental human perception, and as such it was considered by Schilder (1964) to be important in the development of body-image. Schilder has stated, "Two factors, apparently, play a special part in the creation of body-image. The one is pain, the other the motor control over our limbs" (p. 104). The role of pain in the reformation of the body-image following illness or disability is totally unknown at this time.

White and Sweet (1955) have stated the interplay of pain and emotion as follows:

> Pain and its relief constitute one of the great problems of medicine. Both in the production of pain and its treatment psychological factors are of great importance. 'Real pain' cannot be distinguished from 'imaginary pain' because the only true pain to the patient is what he feels. No other person can judge the intensity accurately. Individual reaction to pain varies enormously. Hypnosis, suggestion, placebo, and distraction can relieve both 'real pain' and 'imaginary pain.' It is our experience that patients complaining of pain almost always have a physiological basis for the complaint, although neurotic mechanisms may greatly exaggerate the suffering (p. 115).

It has also been pointed out by White and Sweet (1955) that when activity and attention are turned from somatic preoccupation to other things, the best analgesic is achieved. Application of this principle is well-known in therapeutics, but in vocational rehabilitation, for example, the placement and employment of the person who complains of persistent pain are viewed as a difficult problem. On the other hand, it might well be that vocational rehabilitation would provide the solution to the individual's pain and suffering by rechanneling activity and attention in other directions.

Other factors related to actual physical dimensions of disability which may be important in determining emotional behavior are those of the severity or degree of disability and visibility or the obviousness of the impairment. Wright (1960) is uncertain as to the effect of these two variables, although she considers visibility only in regard to reactions others may have to the disabled.

> It may be postulated that a person with a mild disability may, because he is *almost* normal, have a greater push to hide and deny his disability, thereby thwarting his own adjustment, whereas a person whose disability is so severe as to be undeniable has little recourse but to grapple with the problem of accepting himself as a person with a disability . . . On the other hand it may also be postulated that a mild disability, by imposing fewer frustrations owing to the barrier of physical limitations, makes adjustment easier (p. 53).

> It might be postulated that visible handicaps are especially potent insofar as they present the person to others *first* in terms of his physique and thereby condition subsequent impressions (p. 123).

I think we will have to give weight now, however, to findings which implicate the severity of disability as one among many determinants of emotional behavior, although the evidence still remains somewhat inconsistent. In sensory loss, for example, studies of visually handicapped have not indicated the degree of impairment to be especially significant (Bauman, 1954; Greenberg & Jordan, 1957). Myklebust (1964) has, on the other hand, interpreted his own and many others' results with hearing losses to be that, "The results indicated a relationship between this sensory deprivation and emotional adjustment. The age of onset, the degree of hearing loss, and sex were found to be significant variables affecting this relationship" (p. 156).

Smits (1965) has recently reported that among a sample of physically handicapped adolescents, those with more severe disabilities had significantly less favorable self-concepts. Visibility was not investigated in this study as a factor of emotional adjustment, but rather as a factor of sociometric status within a larger group. Smits' 201 subjects were not homogeneous in disability, and severity of disability was judged on the basis of broad categories into which his subjects were divided.

The most noteworthy and exacting investigation relating emotional behavior to degree of disability has been contributed by Moos and Solomon (1965). They studied forty-nine female rheumatoid arthritic patients who were carefully diagnosed and classed as to their degree of functional incapacity. Comparisons were made between groups primarily on the basis of eighty-eight special scales derived from the MMPI, although structured interviews and ratings of various sorts were included in studies of the same patients. Moos and Solomon found in their series of patients that those with greater degrees of functional incapacity were also those with more physical symptoms and complaints, greater depression and apathy, and increased neurotic tendencies toward isolation, anxiety, dependency and lack of behavorial control. A similar study by Wallen *et al.* (1964) has employed a group of sixty-six orthopedically disabled adults who were successful rehabilitants grossly classified as to severity of disability. Their principal finding was that the mildly disabled tended to direct their guilt and hostility outward against the environment and had higher anxiety levels, whereas the severely disabled internalized these feelings. Wallen *et al.* remark that both groups showed a high incidence of emotional disturbance as measured by the MMPI. There were many problems in sampling recognized by the authors in this study and they have not recommended generalization of their findings. These results might, however, suggest the hypothesis that emotional stability in the physically disabled is not necessarily a requisite for vocational rehabilitation. All of their subjects were successful rehabilitants, and yet the group showed a high incidence of emotional disturbance. This may well have been an artifact.

Research has been conducted with patients having spinal cord lesions, attempting to relate the degree of functional incapacity to emotional adjustment (Wittkower, *et al.*, 1954; Seymore, 1955). These studies have not produced significant information, having relied on the level of the lesion of their subjects as the sole index of the degree of functional incapacity and dealing with their findings in a very generalized manner. Wittkower, *et al.*, for example, studied fifty paraplegic and quadriplegic patients by means of psychiatric interviews and psychological tests. However, interpretation of the findings was given in generalities about reactions to disability, social, occupational, and economic situations without clear explanation of their source or substantiation. Seymore's study of twenty-five paraplegics and twenty-five quadriplegics utilized ratings of personal and social adjustment which may have been influenced by considerable bias on the part of the judges as so often happens in research of this type. No appreciable differences were detected between Seymore's groups, with the exception that the quadriplegics were rated somewhat more favorably in social adjustment. Barron's (1955) study attempting to differentiate groups with visible and non-visible disabilities was a unique and needed one, but it suffered from a different kind of research problem in that insufficient agreement was obtained among the judges used to evaluate patients.

Our knowledge of the effects of degree of functional incapacity and visibility of physical impairment upon emotional behavior is seriously limited by vast differences in methodology and quality of research. Tizzard (1962) and Moos (1964) have pointed out in their critical reviews the kinds of difficulties that must curtail the pronouncement of any general principles of these relationships at the present time. Cautions of this kind do not seem to have much effect, however, since practitioners in rehabilitation fields still tend to use research results uncritically, and research tends to repeat the same errors time after time. This is a major reason for eliminating a discussion of personality patterns and specific disabilities in this chapter.

Before ending the present discussion, however, particular attention will be paid to two especially relevant and commonly occurring emotional responses to severe illness and disability. The following section will consider what facts are known about depression and denial, which are best approached not as personality characteristics of the chronically ill and disabled but as adaptive mechanisms by which individuals attempt to resolve a threatening and largely unexpected change in their lives. It is especially necessary to remember that these mechanisms operate in physically and psychologically intact persons, although perhaps to a less dramatic degree.

DEPRESSION AND DENIAL

There are many synonyms used to describe the depressive reactions frequently observed in the chronically ill and disabled such as mourning, dejection, despair, grief, etc. However we choose to label these reactions, the clinical picture is usually much the same and has long been a source of concern to those attempting to provide rehabilitation. Cleghorn and Curtis (1959) have concisely described the clinical manifestations of a wide variety of behavior patterns which come under the global term of "depression." According to these authors, the kind of depressive reaction typically seen to occur in chronic illness and disability varies in intensity and duration with age, sex, cultural background and other factors. The incidence rate appears to rise sharply from early adulthood to senility with the rate for women being somewhat higher than for men by about three to two. We do not know how well these factors fit the situation of the disabled, however, since careful studies are almost totally lacking.

The principal clinical manifestations of these reactions as outlined by Cleghorn and Curtis are the following: (1) reduced

spontaneous movement and verbalization, (2) mood of hopelessness and self-depreciation, (3) insomnia, loss of appetite,
weight loss, constipation, (4) reduced or absent sexual function,
(5) incapacity for physical or mental effort, and (6) increased
somatic complaints.

Turning now to Wright's (1955) description of the "mourning" reaction to illness and disability we find somewhat the
same clinical description in a different jargon. Wright (pp.
57-60) remarks upon the following symptoms: (1) a sudden
and massive constriction of the life space, (2) unimpaired capacities are ignored, (3) preoccupation with loss, (4) gradual
abatement following reconstruction of self-concept and body-
image, (5) severity determined by values affected by loss, (6)
mood of hopelessness, worthlessness, (7) perceptions dominated
by premorbid comparisons. Wright believes that the "mourning" response to illness and disability is necessary and perhaps
beneficial and should not be counteracted too early. Mourning
implies a realization of loss and is the beginning of "the development of new coping mechanisms for the acquisition of new
motivations and for changes in values which are necessary in
the process of overcoming mourning" (Wright, p. 59-60). Central
to the whole adjustment process characterized clinically by
mourning is a reconstruction of the individual's self-concept
and body-image.

It has become rather widely accepted in rehabilitation that
depression or mourning is equated with a "realistic" realization of loss and facilitates recovery, while denial of disability
is the antithesis and interferes with rehabilitation. Wright's
(1960) theory holds that, "There is good reason to believe
that the period of mourning can be a healing period during
which the wound is first anesthetized and then gradually
closed, leaving the least scarring" (p. 114). However, Wright
also recognizes that the "psychological value of mourning" is
yet to be demonstrated. "The issue is by no means closed, for

there is hardly enough study to permit conclusive statements" (1960, p. 115). Let us, therefore, take a closer look at the research on the subject of depression in the chronically ill and disabled, coming a bit later to the subject of denial of disability.

There is no point mentioning all of the references for all types of physical disability that have implicated depression as a highly significant emotional response. The list would be almost endless. Only some of the generalizable and well-founded research will be discussed. It should be mentioned before proceeding that depressive symptoms are not only seen as emotional responses to disability, but probably influence the course of disease and recovery as well. Ripley (1950) has shown this, for example, in glaucoma patients. Ripley studied a small series of eighteen persons to investigate the relation of emotional reactions and intraocular pressure by means of interviews, observations, and appropriate physical measures. In all of Ripley's subjects there was a history of anxiety, anger, or depression associated with a frustrating situation at the time of onset. "It was repeatedly found that increased severity of eye symptoms and elevation of intraocular pressure coincided with accentuation of previously existing frustrations or the development of new threats to the patient's security" (p. 525). This research bore out earlier suggestions of this relationship dating back to 1818. Similarly, Schmale (1958) has studied 42 patients hospitalized either for acute process or exacerbation of chronic disease, as well as family members' reports, showing that in virtually all of this group there was evidence of actual, threatened, or symbolic object loss. Emotional reactions with feelings of helplessness and hopelessness were especially prevalent immediately prior to onset. In dealing with depression and related symptoms, then, we are faced with an extremely far-reaching pervasive problem in rehabilitation. The recent literature contains many statements relating the least favorable disease course and frequent exacerbations in cardiac disease, multiple sclerosis, tuberculosis, rheumatoid arthritis, diabetes and malignancy to depressive symptomatology and stressful life situations (see Mason, 1961).

The dynamics of depression or mourning due to chronic disease and disability have never had a satisfactory explanation. To state that this is the logical consequence of a realistic realization of loss which has been sustained seems to me to be a happy misrepresentation which tends to lull clinicians into ignoring the response. Maintaining that this response is somehow beneficial is likewise avoiding the problem. A more reasonable explanation, at least inferentially, and one which prompts us to seek more information, is one offered by Moos and Solomon (1965). They maintain, largely as a result of their research with rheumatoid arthritics, that the failure of more efficient defensive measures against the threat of disability, the generation of high levels of anxiety and depression, and increased functional incapacity go hand in hand. Following this reasoning, depression does not facilitate adjustment and acceptance of disability, but leads to increasing disability if not interrupted.

There are indications that depressive reactions are transitory and situational in traumatic disabilities such as paraplegia (Mueller, 1962) and are rarely prolonged or exaggerated. However, extensive study in chronic illness (Dovenmuehle & Verwoerdt, 1962, 1963; Verwoerdt & Dovenmuehle, 1964) suggest that these reactions may persist for years and are especially significant in cardiac disease. Since the work of these authors is the most thorough and comprehensive on the subject of depression and illness, I have chosen theirs to review most extensively. Most of their findings are concisely summarized in Verwoerdt and Dovenmuehle (1964).

Basing their research on persons with heart disease, Verwoerdt and Dovenmuehle state unequivocally that "A cluster of depressive episodes and the intensity of unpleasant affect during the depressive period determine the extent of disability for life activities" (p. 857). Some of their specific findings, however, will be more helpful. These authors have reported that depressive symptoms occur in about two-thirds of their patients, usually associated with lowered self-esteem and increased anxiety (Dovenmuehle & Verwoerdt, 1962). Also among the more significant findings reported by these investigators are that the severity of illness is not directly related to the development of depression (Dovenmuehle & Verwoerdt, 1963; Verwoerdt & Dovenmuehle, 1964). The severity of the disease did not influence the severity of depression, both mild and severe conditions having the same power in provoking depressive symptoms. While this might seem to contradict the previous suggestion that severity of disability is a factor in emotional response, it was further reported that in mild conditions depression cleared gradually, but in more severe cases the depression might last for years. "In more severe cases, however, frequent painful symptoms may prevent the reactivation of hope and optimism, resulting in chronic depressive affect" (Verwoerdt & Dovenmuehle, 1964).

The frequency of hospitalization, also unrelated to severity of disease, was found related to depression (Dovenmuehle & Verwoerdt, 1963; Verwoerdt & Dovenmuehle, 1964). More frequent hospitalizations generate more severe depressions. This effect is attributed to the situational stress and isolation inherent in hospitalization. The authors conclude:

> Hospitalization, immobilization, and the idea of having heart disease may alter the concept of self and result in a depressive reaction, making specific rational countermeasures necessary. Once the patient's concept of himself has become changed permanently and he has incorporated the conviction that he is disabled, he is likely to continue functioning at an unduly low level. Depressive feelings may then reinforce this downward spiral, and any psychological or physical distress provides further proof to him of his disability (Verwoerdt & Dovenmuehle, p. 861).

Clearly, we should not underestimate the importance of emotional responses such as depression in rehabilitation, but we also may see another relatively common response referred to as "denial of disability." Depression and denial appear to be opposite sides of the coin, although both mechanisms are obviously defensive measures against the threat of disability. It has even been possible recently to make a fine distinction between these two reactions on the basis of adrenocortical activity, a sensitive index of response to stress.

Friedman, Mason, and Hamburg (1963) have reported a study involving 43 parents of children critically ill and hospitalized with leukemia. These subjects were in a state of chronic stress and were studied over an extended period during the child's hospitalization, both in residence in a ward of the hospital and at home. Periods of acute stress, such as changes in the child's condition due to cardiac arrest or massive hemorrhage, were also superimposed. The results were striking in that although sex differences were significant, subjects maintained a high but constant rate of cortico-steroid excretion which persisted even with added acute stress.

A wide range of coping behavior was observed in these parents, including all physical activities and psychological processes that served to reduce the disturbance of stress. These investigators state, "It would appear from our clinical evaluation that the subjects with lower mean 17-OHCS levels were individuals who might be considered well defended, or relatively well buffered, from the impact of stressful situation, regardless of the type of defenses utilized" (Friedman et al., p. 374).

Individuals were selected for special study who showed maximum overt and verbal denials of their child's prognosis. It was found that, "Without exception, the mean corticosteroid values for the individuals showing marked denial mechanisms are among the very lowest" (Friedman, et al., p. 375). This aroused the investigators' curiosity so that another series of parents were studied, paying particular attention to their defenses.

Wolff, Friedman, Hafer, and Mason (1964) attempted to test the idea that individuals whose defenses are effective in keeping psychic tension low will have lower mean corticosteroid excretion rates, and the less effective the defenses, the higher the rate. Both mothers and fathers were divided into high, medium, and low groups on the basis of observed cortico-steroid values, and it was found that there was a significant correlation between rated defense effectiveness and steroid excretion rates. The correlation was much higher and more significant for men.

The typical "high" was described by Wolff *et al.* as (1) showing considerable emotional distress, (2) difficulty in maintaining composure during interview, (3) relating experiences in an obviously painful manner, and (4) expressing feelings of dread, hopelessness and helplessness. The typical "low" (1) was well-organized and highly controlled, (2) made extensive use of denial, (3) showed minimal anxiety with no expression of guilt and (4) appeared slightly euphoric and unrealistically optimistic. The clinical picture of depression, anxiety and emotional distress at one extreme and denial and unrealistic optimism at the other provided by these studies corresponds quite closely with patients' reactions observed in rehabilitation. It also appears that while neither depression nor denial may facilitate rehabilitation or recovery, denial is effective in reducing the effects of stress, although the least mobilizing response. As has been pointed out before and will be again, a moderate degree of emotional arousal is essential for effective learning and adaptation. Neither excessive arousal (depression) nor very low levels (denial) are conducive to adjustment.

The type of psychoendocrine study just mentioned has been found useful in longitudinal investigations of patient affect in relation to treatment stresses at the University of Colorado

Medical Center (McDaniel, 1968). Twenty-one recently injured and admitted paraplegic patients were studied in their mood and behavior, plasma corticosteroid and urinary catecholamine excretion rates during selected periods of objective stress during a hospitalization and treatment period of 90 days. The general correlation between depression, anxiety levels, and the use of denial with endocrine functions reported by others was confirmed also in these patients. It was also found that various aspects of mood and behavior such as depression, anxiety level, irritability, physical complaints, defensiveness, etc., were differentially effected by transition from one stage to another during the course of treatment and rehabilitation. The psychoendocrine approach itself seems to have particular merit as a "natural history" method of investigation of affective responses during rehabilitation.

Most of us find it easier to understand the occurrence of depression than perhaps the equally prevalent denial of disability or the handicapping effects of disability. Weinstein and Kahn (1955), who have reported the most comprehensive investigation of denial, state that although denial of illness or disability may be expressed in various ways, five major expressions may be noticed. These are, (1) complete denial in which patients deny that they are ill in any respect, (2) denial of major disability in which major incapacities are denied and less threatening aspects of illness are stressed, (3) minimization of disability or illness or attribution to some benign cause, (4) projection of ownership of the illness, or (5) temporal displacement in which patients admit illness or disability in the past but not in the present.

Weinstein and Kahn (1953, 1955) have also studied the premorbid personalities of "deniers" by means of interviews with relatives, friends, and employers finding that they had been somewhat compulsive and perfectionistic. They seemed to have always regarded illness as an imperfection or weakness.

Friedlander (1967) has recently put together a convincing argument for considering denial responses, or "anosognosia" as commonly encountered in hemiplegia, as a perceptual disturbance. This author states that conceptions of denial have traditionally been in the vein of a perceptual defect or a defect in body-image or a maladaptation to illness. Friedlander himself feels, however, that all three points of view may be legitimately combined.

> I believe a theory can reasonably be constructed for the anosognosic syndrome in which all these various explanations are utilized. The patients have a particular type of personality, one which has utilized denial of illness in their pre-morbid state. There is then damage to the brain which results in: (1) parietal lobe damage or at least damage to that part or parts of the brain which have to do with the correct synthesis of multiple perceptions, and (2) confusion with loss of some ability for reality testing (p. 1406).

We return now to a premise that has been expressed many times, i.e., depression denotes a realization of loss and facilitates rehabilitation, while denial is an unrealistic emotional response and an interference. Intuitively, this statement may seem correct, yet outside of one preliminary study by Caron (1959) it has no objective support. Caron has studied 25 patients having first heart attacks and reached the tentative conclusion that early depression precluded later excessive disability in terms of mood disturbance, non-cooperation, self-esteem loss, and work incapacity. Patients denying disabling effects were found one year later to be excessively disabled. Caron has thus tentatively confirmed the widely-held belief that the prognosis for ultimate rehabilitation is better for patients who face the reality of the situation and show an initial period of depression. I doubt, however, that when sufficient research has been accomplished either of these responses will have been found to be favorable for the rehabilitation of the chronically ill and disabled.

This brings us to the final consideration of the importance of emotional factors in physical disability and rehabilitation. The question to be answered is what specific influences do emotional responses have in the process of rehabilitation and treatment.

INFLUENCE OF EMOTIONAL AROUSAL IN REHABILITATION

A case in point in this relation is an early study reported by Ruesch (1946) in which 123 out-patients and 64 in-patients who showed "delayed recovery" were studied. Patients who were suffering a wide variety of physical diseases and injuries were evaluated by means of medical and psychiatric examinations, social and cultural factors, and with psychological tests. These were cases who did not recover from acute or chronic disease, had multiple diseases or operations in succession, suffered intermittently from the same disease, or had permanent physical symptoms without corresponding objective findings. Ruesch reported cases of delayed recovery to be related to (1) the simultaneous occurrence of psychological disturbances and disease, (2) situational changes connected with illness, and (3) poor medical management and treatment of psychogenic symptoms.

More recently, Vernier, *et al.* (1961) have obtained results with 767 male veterans with pulmonary tuberculosis concerning the relation of emotional factors and response to medical treatment, hospital adjustment and community adjustment. Their results were not in any way surprising and indicated that those with freedom from emotional disturbances such as severe anxiety, neurotic or depressive reactions were most likely to make appropriate hospital and community adjustments and to respond more favorably to treatment.

Two investigations (Goldsmith, 1956; Smith & Fink, 1963) are singled out for discussion because of their unusually detailed approach. Goldsmith's subjects were thirty male paraplegics without previous rehabilitation who were studied while in a program of routine medical care, physical therapy, occupational therapy, and counseling. After three and one-half months of treatment, subjects were rated by physicians and therapists as to progress. All but three patients could be placed in either a "much improved" or "little improved" category from ratings, and these groups were compared on the basis of psychological test data. Goldsmith's conclusion was that an "active upset" with need to remedy their situation as well as strong aggressive feelings and optimistic attitudes facilitated rehabilitation. On the contrary, internalized aggression, dependency, self-punishment, and pessimism led to little improvement during rehabilitation. The research reported by Smith and Fink attempted to correlate changes in physical mobility and performance in activities of daily living with psychological variables, including Q-sort descriptions of patients' personal and social adjustment and motivation. There were some relationships detected which, in order of their suggested importance, were "motivation," personal adjustment, orientation and intelligence. By a statistical weighing of these variables the authors were able to derive a system which correctly classified 87.9% of their patients as improved or non-improved.

Studies of the types just cited are significant to rehabilitation because they will eventually enable us to predict at the beginning of treatment which patients will need particular attention and special effort for rehabilitation to succeed. Based on the best information we presently have available, special effort is needed for those patients and clients who (1) have concurrent psychological and physical symptoms, (2) have situational changes which complicate their illness, or (3) show either excessively high or excessively low levels of emotional arousal.

The picture will hopefully be completed by further investigation.

Then, too, we must recognize that the procedures designed to alleviate disabling conditions do not always bring the relief that we anticipate. Studies following the correction of cardiac defects, congenital cataracts and epilepsy by surgery (Kaplan, 1956; von Senden, 1960; Ferguson & Rayport, 1965) indicate that removal of disability is not universally reacted to favorably. Ferguson and Rayport report the following postoperative course in many such cases:

> The profile of the postoperative course after cardiac surgery and after operation for congenital blindness is similar to that observed after temporal lobe excision. In the early postoperative period, there is enthusiasm over new-found health, comfort, and abilities. Then follows a period of crisis. The person with new vision, for instance, finds that he is exposed not only to a flood of new sensory impressions but, like the former cardiac and epileptic, he is deluged with intra and interpersonal demands; he is 'burdened with normality.' All of these patients are involved in what may be called an 'acute maturational phase.' To fully realize the benefits of surgery, they must enter upon a reeducative period (p. 35).

This research illustrates quite well a point made earlier in this chapter that any sudden change, whether positive or negative, physical or situational, introduces uncertainty and, as a result, increased emotional arousal. Response to change is conditioned by the nature and extent of the change and the number and kinds of concepts which require modification in order to adapt to the change. Excessive emotional arousal makes efficient adaptation difficult, although some degree of arousal is necessary to "drive" the person towards adaptation.

Truly, there is a complex interaction between emotional factors, illness and disability, and response to rehabilitation and treatment. We have only a very few of the answers at present and a great many more questions. Now that behavioral research in rehabilitation has become fashionable and popular, we can expect immense changes to occur; indeed some are now occurring, not only in practice but also in the education and training of rehabilitation professionals.

If this chapter concerning emotional factors has any merit at all, it is not in drawing together as much useful information as may be possible in the near future, but in suggesting some relationships which I believe to be important and which tend to be overlooked in many research and clinical efforts. Relationships which may have a crucial bearing on the approach of rehabilitation fields to their task are not well known, but for an unusually systematic and well-documented general approach to emotional and physiological functioning the reader is referred to Mason (1961).

References

Axelrod, S.   Effects of early blindness: Performance of blind and sighted children on tactile and auditory tasks. 1959, *Res. Monogr. No. 7* Amer. Found. Blind, New York

Barker, R., Wright, B. & Gonick, M. *Adjustment to Physical Handicap and Illness: A Survey of the Social Psychology of Physique and Disability*. 1946, Soc. Sci. Res. Council, New York.

Barron, J. Physical handicap and personality: Study of the seen versus the unseen disabilities. *Arch. PM&R.*, 1955, 36, 639-43.

Bauman, M. *Adjustment to Blindness*. 1954, St. Council Blind, Dept. Welfare, Commonwealth of Penn.

Caron, H. The Crisis Factor in illness and Disability. 1959, Cleveland Sympos. Behav. Res. Rehabil. Summ.

Cleghorn, R. & Curtis, G. *Depression, Mood, Symptom, Syndrome.* 1959, Geigy, Basle.

Cohen, A. Personality aspects of epileptic seizures. A review of the literature from 1950 through 1961. *J. Rehab.*, 1962, 28, 18-20.

DeWolfe, A., Barrell, R. & Cummings, J. Patient variables in emotional response to hospitalization for physical illness. *J. Consult. Psychol.*, 1966, 30, 68-72.

Dovenmuehle, R. & Verwoerdt, A. Physical illness and depressive symptomatology I. Incidence of depressive symptoms in hospitalized cardiac patients. *J. Amer. Geriat. Soc.*, 1962, 10, 932-47.

Dovenmuehle, R. & Verwoerdt, A. Physical illness and depressive symptomatology II. Factors of length and severity of illness and frequency of hospitalization. *J. Gerontol.*, 1963, 18, 260-6.

Ferguson, S. & Rayport, M. The adjustment to living without epilepsy. *J. Nerv. Ment. Dis.*, 1965, 140, 26-37.

Freedman, S., Grunebaum, H. & Greenblatt, M. Perceptual and cognitive changes in sensory deprivation. In *Sensory Deprivation*, 1961, Harvard Press, Cambridge, Mass.

Freidman, S., Mason, J. & Hamburg, D.   Urinary 17-hydroxycorti-
    costeroid levels in parents of children with neoplastic disease.
    Psychosom. Med., 1963, **25**, 364-76.

Friedlander, W.   Anosognosia and perception, *Amer. J. Phys. Med.*,
    1967, **46**, 1394-1408.

Goldsmith, H.   Contributions of certain personality characteristics
    to degree of improvement in rehabilitation. *Diss. Abstr.*, 1956,
    16, 1504.

Greenberg, H. & Jordon, S.   Differential effects of total blindness
    and partial sight on several personality traits. *Except. Child.*,
    1957, **24**, 123-4.

Harrower, M. & Kraus, J.   Psychological studies on patients with
    multiple sclerosis. *Arch. Neurol. Psychiat.*, 1951, **66**, 44-57.

Heron, W. The pathology of boredom. In *Frontiers of Psychological
    Research.* (Coppersmith, Ed.), 1966, Freeman, San Francisco.

Hohmann, G.   Some effects of spinal cord lesions on experienced
    emotional feelings. *Psychophysiol.*, 1966, **3**, 143-156.

Kaplan, S.   Psychological aspects of cardiac disease: A study of
    patients experiencing mitral commissurotomy. *Psychosom. Med.*,
    1956, **18**, 221-33.

Krause, E. On the Time and Place of Crises. 1964, New Eng. Rehab.
    Cent., Boston (mimeo).

Mason, R.   *Internal Perception and Bodily Functioning.* 1961,
    International Universities Press, New York.

McDaniel, J. Depression and Steroids in Paraplegic Patients. In SRS
    Project RT-10, Progress report No. 4, Univ. Colo. School
    Med., Denver, 1968 (mimeo).

Melzack, R.   The perception of pain. *Sci. Amer.*, 1961, **204**, 41-9.

Melzack, R. & Wall, P.   Pain mechanisms: A new theory. *Science*,
    1965, **150**, 971-9.

Mendelson, J., Kubzansky, P., Liederman, P., Wexler, D. & Solomon, P. Physiological and psychological aspects of sensory deprivation: A case analysis. In *Sensory Deprivation*, 1961, Harvard Press, Cambridge, Mass.

Moos, R. Personality factors associated with rheumatoid arthritis: A review. *J. Chron. Dis.*, 1964, 17, 41-55.

Moos, R. & Solomon, G. Personality correlates to the degree of functional incapacity of patients with physical disease. *J. Chron. Dis.*, 1965, 18, 1019-38.

Mueller, A. Psychologic factors in rehabilitation of paraplegic patients. *Arch. PM&R.*, 1962, 43, 151-9.

Myklebust, H. *The Psychology of Deafness.* 1964, Grune & Stratton, New York.

Parsons, T. Definitions of health and illness in the light of American values and social structure. In *Patients, Physicians and Illness.* (Jaco, Ed.) 1958, Chap. 20, pp. 165-87.

Ploski, H., Levita, E. & Riklan, M. Impairment of voluntary movement in Parkinson's Disease in relation to activation level, autonomic malfunction, and personality rigidity. *Psychosom. Med.*, 1966, 28, 70-7.

Rainer, J., Altshuler, K., Kallman, F. & Deming, W. (Eds.) *Family and Mental Health Problems in a Deaf Population.* 1963, Columbia University, New York

Riklan, M. & Levita, E. Psychological studies in parkinsonism: Effects of subcortical surgery. *J. Gerontol.*, 1966, 21, 372-9.

Ripley, H. Life situations, emotions and glaucoma. In *Life Stress and Bodily Disease*, 1951, Res. Publ. Assoc. Nerv. Ment. Dis., New York.

Ruesch, J. Chronic disease and psychological invalidism. 1946, *Psychosom. Med. Monogr.*, Amer. Soc. Res. Psychosom. Probs., New York.

Schilder, P. *The Image and Appearance of the Human Body.* 1950, Wiley, New York.

Schmale, A. Relationship of separation and depression to disease. *Psychosom. Med.*, 1958, **20**, 259-77.

Seymore, C. Personality and paralysis: Comparative adjustment of paraplegics and quadriplegics. *Arch. PM&R.*, 1955, **36**, 691-4.

Shontz, F., Fink, S. & Hallenbeck, C. Chronic physical illness as threat. *Arch. PM&R.*, 1960, **41**, 143-7.

Simmel, M. Phantoms, phantom pain and "denial." *Amer. J. Psychother.*, 1959, **13**, 603-13.

Smith, J. & Fink, S. The relationship between physical improvement and psychological factors in chronically ill patients. *J. Clin. Psychol.*, 1963, **19**, 289-92.

Smits, S. The reactions of self and others to the obviousness and severity of physical disability. *Rehab. Couns. Bull.*, 1965, **9**, 41-6

Sterritt, G., Camp, B. & Lipman, B. Effects of early auditory deprivation upon auditory and visual information processing. *Percept. Mot. Skills*, 1966, **23**, 123-30.

Thume, L. & Murphree, O. Acceptance of the white cane and hope for the restoration of sight in blind persons as an indicator of adjustment. *J. Clin. Psychol.*, 1961, **17**, 208-09.

Tizzard, B. The personality of epileptics: A discussion of the evidence. *Psychol. Bull.*, 1962, **59**, 196-210.

Vernier, C., Barrell, R., Cummings, J., Dickinson, J. & Hooper, H. Psychosocial study of the patient with pulmonary tuberculosis. *Psychol. Monogr.*, 1961, **75**, 1-30.

Verwoerdt, A. & Dovenmuehle, R. Heart disease and depression. *Geriat.*, 1964, **18**, 856-64.

von Senden, M. *Space and Sight.* 1960, Free Press, Glencoe, Ill.

Wallen, N., Samuelson, C., Brewer, J., Gerber, S. & Woolaver, J. A comparison of slightly and severely orthopedically disabled and "normal" adults on several psychological tests. *Rehab. Couns. Bull.*, 1964, **8**, 50-7.

Weinstein, S., Vetter, R. & Sersen, E. Physiological and Experiential Concomitants of the Phantom.1964, Albert Einstein Coll. Med., New York, final report, VRA proj. No. 427 (mimeo).

Weinstein, E. & Kahn, R. Personality factors in denial of illness. *Arch. Neurol. Psychiat.*, 1953, **69**, 355-67.

Weinstein, E. & Kahn, R. *Denial of Illness.* 1955, Thomas, Springfield, Ill.

Wenger, M., Jones, F., & Jones, M. *Physiological Psychology.* 1956, Holt, Rinehart & Winston, New York.

White, J. & Sweet, W. *Pain, Its Mechanisms and Neurosurgical Control.* 1955, Thomas, Springfield, Ill.

Wittkower, E., Gingras, G., Mergler, L., Wigdor, B. & Lepine, A. A combined psychosocial study of spinal cord lesions. *Canad. Med. Assoc. J.*, 1954, **71**, 109-15.

Wolff, C., Freidman, S., Hofer, M. & Mason, J. Relationship between psychological defenses and mean urinary 17-OHCS excretion rates: I. A predictive study of parents of fatally ill children. *Psychosom. Med.*, 1964, **26**, 576-91.

Wright, B. *Physical Disability: A Psychological Approach.* 1960, Harper, New York.

Wright, E. The period of mourning in chronic illness. In *Medical and Psychological Teamwork in the Care of the Chronically Ill.* (Harrower,Ed.)1955, Thomas, Springfield, Ill.

Chapter IV

SENSORY AND PERCEPTUAL PROCESSES IN DISABILITY

THIS CHAPTER will break a very old precedent that has been set by many writers on this subject, that of cataloging and discussing perceptual defects and disorders characteristic of neurological impairments. That approach has only seemed to generate research designed to identify perceptual deficits and somehow has prevented us from dealing with broader issues and implications for behavior. Therefore, certain selected aspects of perceptual processes operating not only in the physically disabled, but for the most part among the non-disabled as well, have been singled out for examination. These are general perceptual issues which seem to be common among several disability categories and are consequently considered to be more appropriate subjects for this discussion than specific neurological conditions.

BODY-IMAGE

The first perceptual factor which will be considered is that of the body-image and disturbances in this perception due to physical impairment. There has been considerable interest in rehabilitation in this perceptual phenomenon and there is some diverse investigation on the subject which might be brought together.

Historically, the modern concept of the body-image seems to have arisen with Sir Henry Head who through his clinical experience evolved the idea of a neurological schema developed from postural and tactile experiences and capable of modifying present experience. Paul Schilder's later concept, while dealing heavily in symbolic relationships, enlarged upon this basic idea to include not only internal and external sensations but also the orientation of the body in space. Subsequent authors have utilized this concept in relation to personality (Fisher & Cleveland, 1958). There is no reason to doubt Schilder's opinion that the body-image is a most fundamental human concept and that sensations and perceptions may be interpreted and integrated into experience on the basis of this concept. However, the body-image should be placed in its proper perspective, as Wright (1960) does, as an element of the individual's self-cognition and perception rather than as an inclusive entity itself. Shontz (1964) after extensive research and review of the data available concludes that the hypothetical construct of "body-image" has not been adequately demonstrated but nevertheless provides the following rationale for its existence:

> A person's own body possesses psychological properties that set it apart from most other stimuli. Under normal conditions the body is the focus of an individual's identity, and its limits define, more or less clearly, a boundary that separates him from his environment. One's body is the only perceptual object that remains phenomenally constant, despite developmental and accidental alterations. It is the only object that completely corresponds, spatially and temporally, with personal existence. It yields experiences that cannot be directly shared with others, and it forms a nucleus, around which the developing structure of personal values synthesized (p. 1).

It should also be recognized that body-image does not occupy a large proportion of our conscious experience. It is largely a product of internal perception which is not consistently the focus of attention. Mason (1961) has pointed out that in terms of the distribution of "awareness" or attention, human experience is devoted primarily to external stimuli, somewhat less to our own thought processes (memory, planning, etc.) and least of all to internal perception. Internal perception is largely undifferentiated experience and only becomes differentiated when we become aware of "feeling" associated with internal sensations (Mason, 1961).

As an element of the individual's perception of himself, the body-image has all the properties of the self-concept as outlined by Carl Rogers (1947, 1951) who suggests that the self-concept (1) develops out of the organism's interaction with the environment, (2) may incorporate the values of others, (3) strives for consistency, (4) rejects inconsistent experience and (5) changes as a result of maturation and learning. Body-image then is a construct which, like other self-perceptions, is a product of relevant experiences and exerts an organizing force upon behavior.

The organizing process which permits perception and learning requires a complex system of analysis, probability weighting, memory, programming, and testing as in the system described by Pribram (1961). It is important to remember that a perception, (a), does not occur as a direct representation of an object, (A), but is a prediction or "best estimate" of the kind of object which could have generated the particular pattern of stimuli. Percepts do not persist because they are "true" or "absolute," but because they are successful predictions. We, therefore, have constancy and stability only as long as our perceptions continue to be confirmed. Any change in stimulus pattern generated by an object (including the body) must be evaluated and, if significant, incorporated into a modified percept. Any experience which is not consistent or does not match the established model, whether positive or negative, pleasant or unpleasant, is accompanied by increased arousal and must be accommodated if evaluated as being significant. Obviously the process does not bother with minor variations and transitory changes since perceptual constancy would be impossible under such circumstances. Behavior would be continually disorganized if we constantly had to modify our concepts. For this reason, the human organism has an inherent tendency to resist change and to be excited by the unexpected.

Based upon the preceding inferences, we would expect any significant and enduring change in experiences or sensations relevant to the body to produce a corresponding change in the "body-image" and in total self-perception. A modified body-image, if an accurate representation or estimate, should reflect relevant changes.

As has already been stated, illness and perhaps disability are accompanied by increased somatic preoccupation, focusing of awareness upon physical sensations and changes. As Barker, Wright, and Gonick (1946) have inferred, this is manifest by attention to even minor variations in physiological functioning. There is nothing irrational about this shift in attention for it is a consistent adjustment arising out of the central regulating process of behavior. It is the initial step necessary to modifying concepts and behavior, in this case the body-image , and is an alerted response to an unexpected change that may require decision and action. As has been mentioned previously, Secord and Jourard (1953) have demonstrated, in physically normal college students, increased somatic concern and lower body satisfaction to be associated. Shontz, Fink, and Hallenbeck (1960) have found tentative support for a shift in attention from social to physical needs in chronically ill patients. Also in a study mentioned earlier, Weinstein, Vetter, and Sersen (1964) have found a normal variation in values attached to body parts (see Table 2) which they attribute partially to changes in cosmetic and functional characteristics of the respective parts. Clearly then, we should expect these perceptual changes.

However, changes in body-image with illness and disability always seem to be referred to as "distortions," even though increased awareness and concern and body-image changes are a necessary consequence. It is also overlooked that a certain amount of "error" in body-image is to be expected since no perception is ever true or absolute but is an estimate that is subject to confirmation and modification. In a sense, every perception is a mistake. The only difference between an illusion and an "accurate" perception is that one is not confirmed by reality, whereas the other is, chances are, a successful prediction of stimulus conditions (Gregory, 1968).

Shontz (1964), having made an extensive review of the research concerning bodily perceptions, concludes that there are many approaches and methods that can be taken which may not be comparable. "Despite a high level of scientific interest in body-image phenomena, it remains to be convincingly demonstrated that significant correlations exist among responses to all reliable instruments that lay legitimate *a priori* claim to the measurement of some aspect of the hypothetical body-image, and there is no compelling reason to accept the assumption that a common causal process underlies all possible modes of personal body cognition" (p. 3). Although Shontz has chosen the method of body-part size judgments, other studies have employed figure drawings, projective techniques, self-ratings, and body-part value ratings. Shontz has demonstrated variation in the body-part size judgments of physically normal college students as a function of sex and the type and location of the body parts estimated. However, this research did not find satisfaction or dissatisfaction with a body part to influence judgment of its size, nor did transistory emotional or situational stress.

It might be expected, if changes in body-image result from physical changes, that this would be reflected in differences in body-part size and preference judgments. This has been investigated by Weinstein, *et al.,* who found that the breast had an equivalent preference rank among 538 women after mastectomy to that of 986 physically intact women. Contrary to controls, however, it was found that the relative preference for the breast increased with age in women after mastectomy. In general, however, Weinstein, *et al.,* have reported a higher relative mean preference for the breast in descending order among normals, unilateral, and bilateral mastectomy samples even though the differences were not statistically significant. In body-part size estimates, some changes have been reported by Fink and Shontz (1960) comparing normal, wheelchair restricted, and hemiplegic persons. It was determined that the physically healthy tended to overestimate, while the disabled underestimated body-part sizes. The authors concluded, "Constriction may be construed to represent a shrinking of the overall body-image, the process occurring because of the loss of sustaining input to the central processing mechanism" (p. 240).

Wachs and Zaks (1960) failed to find any significant differences in the body-images of 30 spinal cord injured men and 30 chronically ill controls, suggesting that there is a general degree of "disturbance" in any chronically ill person. In respect to body-part size perceptions, investigations (Evans, 1962; Bors, 1951) in paraplegia do not report any significant distortion in the perceived length or size of limbs. Both Evans and Fink and Shontz would interpret what changes there are in body perceptions to be due to the disruption of somatic input in chronic illness and disability.

Quite a number of reports have been published calling attention to "distortions" of body-image in the physically disabled based upon interpretation of subject's drawings of human figures. Often the assumption is made in these studies that a distorted drawing reveals a distorted body-image, and that an undistorted drawing reveals an unconscious denial or defensiveness. This, of course, automatically precludes the incorporation of physical changes in the body-image. The greatest degree of "body-image distortion" determined by such studies has been found predominantly in children and adults with sensory and perceptual defects. Abercrombie and Tyson (1966) have recently pointed out in regard to cerebral palsy, however, that such results are more likely due to perceptual distortion in general than to "body-image distortion." In perhaps the most careful study of this type contributed by Centers and Centers (1963), no important differences in the body-images of congenital amputees and non-disabled children were detected.

> It would appear from the analysis of the Draw-A-Person test that the body-images of amputee children, as they are expressed in such drawings, do not differ essentially from those of non-amputee children. When these limbless children are requested to draw a picture of themselves, the majority like non-amputee children represent themselves realistically, since they either leave out the missing limb or include a prosthetic device (Centers & Centers, p. 163).

In regard to body-image and its perception in illness and disability, it seems necessary to exert a different interpretation of the relationship now that some evidence is accumulated. Although synthesis is made difficult by wide differences in methodology and quality of research, it now seems most likely that body-image distortion is due, when it occurs as an extreme under or over emphasis or denial of physical changes, to the disruption of perceptual processes and is but one aspect of perceptual imagery that may be disrupted under these conditions. It is due to inability to process information about change and to assess information accurately in order to organize perceptions accordingly. If there were no perceptual deficit, physical impairment would be accommodated by a modified body-image. Many changes in bodily perceptions accompany chronic illness and disability, but these are probably at least partially due to sensory and social isolation and restricted mobility, all conditions of deprivation that are entirely capable of producing marked disturbances in perceptual processes. In brief, any condition which interferes with the perception and integration of information concerning the body may be expected to be accompanied by body-image distortion, while there is no good reason to suppose body-image distortions in the absence of perceptual difficulties.

That appropriate bodily perceptions are essential for more complex activities and performance is well illustrated by a recent study by Held and Bauer (1967) who have produced some information very much to the point. These investigators reared newborn monkeys in an apparatus designed to eliminate their observing their own body parts, but at the same time allowing for normal developmental activity and care. Infant monkeys placed in this restrictive environment within 12 hours of birth were, for the next 34 days, unable to view any part of their bodies. After 34 days, these subjects were allowed to view one arm and were tested in reaching and grasping attractive objects presented to them for one hour. Normally reared animals would be able to quite accurately reach and manipulate objects before the age of one month. After the first day of testing, the experimental animals were allowed to view the arm for one hour daily for the next 20 days during which their reaching and grasping progressively improved, so that by the end of 20 days of exposure and testing, the animals were proficient in the use of this limb.

Subsequently, the previously unexposed limb was uncovered and the testing and exposure process repeated. Only 10 hours of exposure were required to gain comparable proficiency to the first exposed limb. When both limbs were tested together, the first limb exposed was used in preference to the other. After all testing was completed animals were placed in single cages, and it was noted that, "By the age of 4 months their locomotor behavior was indistinguishable from that of a monkey of comparable age reared under normal laboratory conditions" (p. 720).

At the present time, it is not possible to ascertain the role of body-image "distortions" in rehabilitation, recovery, and physical improvement in persons who have no serious perceptual dysfunction otherwise. Campbell *et al.* (1964) have reported that, while in samples of 29 leg amputees and 27 arm amputees "distortions" in body-image as judged from figure drawings were quite common, this bore no statistically significant relationship to successful prosthetic training. Research will definitely need to continue in this relationship with some serious attempts to reconcile methodological differences. Inferences concerning body-image also serve as one explanation for the occurrence of phantom perceptions as will be seen in the following section concerning this perceptual phenomenon.

The matter of the neurological substrata of the body-image deserves some serious attention, particularly by way of introduction to the following section on phantoms. It appears that a number of people active in research and teaching, not only in psychology but also in physical and occupational therapies (OOTA, 1967), believe the somatosensory homunculus, which in reality is a topologically inaccurate map, to be the genetic neurological framework of the body-image, thus ascribing a specific cerebral locus to this perceptual phenomenon in the post-central gyrus of the cerebrum. Some, such as Simmel (1962), even go so far as to restrict the contribution of sensory information other than tactual and kinesthetic which are inputs to other cortical areas but would logically seem important to bodily perceptions. Simmel has stated, "Thus the stable schema is one that coincides with cortical representation, peripheral innervation ratios, and kinesthetic and tactile experience. The visual components of the schema are less stable" (p. 348). As we have just seen in the research of Held and Bauer, however, visual experience may be equally important to proprioception.

Weinstein, *et al.,* have hypothesized in relation to body-image locus, "We believe that the nucleus of the adult body schema may have its origin in a neural substrate which is the framework for the potential adult sensory homunculus. This neural 'framework' may be modified by multimodal sensory experiences during the lifetime of the organism" (p. 63). Here we find a softer view in that credence is given the multisensory development of bodily experience and perception. However, the conviction is still present that the somatosensory homunculus is the locus of the body-image and that the homunculus itself is a reality rather than a map.

That these sorts of conceptions, based more or less heavily on somatosensory representation in the post-central gyrus, are inadequate must be made clear. First, *only* proprioceptive input is registered in this projection area. Visual, auditory, or other sensory inputs relevant to the body are not analyzed in this area of the cortex and yet are undeniably important components of bodily perceptions and, therefore, body-image. The reactions and values of others likewise enter the picture and determine to some extent the perceptions of our own bodies. Such information is processed perceptually but in no relation to the post-central gyrus. More fundamentally, however, it should be pointed out that a homunculus or graphic representation of projection of somatosensory information is available with differing characteristics for at least four central nervous system areas (Penfield & Jasper, 1954) rather than only one, including the post-central gyrus, second sensory, and supplementary sensory, and lateral and medial ventral nuclei of the thalamus. The latter, of course, is not even cortical but sub-cortical and is probably more nearly the "neurological framework" of body-image than cortical areas, since all extrinsic and intrinsic input sources converge at the level of the thalamus.

Attempts to make such vague hypothetical constructs as "body-image" respectable by assignment to some neural structure may be appealing but are often misleading as well. A certain amount of caution should be exercised in this regard, not only concerning body-image but also for some of the material to follow concerning phantom perceptions.

PHANTOM PERCEPTIONS

The perception of phantom limbs and other body parts is very well documented; its description, according to Simmel's review, dating back to the sixteenth - century French surgeon Ambroise Pare, though the term "phantom" was applied later by S. Weir Mitchell. There are several explanations advanced today for such perceptions (Weinstein, Vetter & Sersen, 1964) and some important variables appear to have been identified. The high incidence of the perceptual phenomenon in certain types of disability, notably amputations and spinal cord injuries, makes this phenomenon of immediate concern in many aspects of rehabilitation. Moreover, as has been pointed out by many writers, phantom perceptions frequently are accompanied by emotional distress, adding to its psychological significance.

Research has not yet established the precise limits of incidence of phantoms, but Table 5 summarizes the findings of several investigators. The phantom perception may or may not be painful, but Weinstein, *et al.* indicate that the perceptions reported by 24% mastectomy cases, 42% limb amputations, and 43% of paraplegics are painful. Some of these eventually end in surgical intervention. Explanations of how such frequent and often painful illusory perceptions occur is therefore a topic of paramount interest.

A fanciful interpretation of the origin of phantom perceptions is that which Weinstein, *et al.* call the "fantasy" of "need" theory. The essence of this viewpoint is that emotional needs for the lost body part or function, or refusal to accept the loss, account for the occurrence of the phantom. The perception is an unconscious defense against the threat of loss. Weinstein,

Table 5

Reported Incidences of Phantoms

Disability Class	Incidence Rate (percentage)	Reference
amputation (limb)	98	Livingston (1945)
	100	Haber (1955)
	100	Weinstein *et al.* (1964)
spinal cord lesions	100	Bors (1951)
	68	Kuhn (1950)
	100	Weinstein *et al.* (1964)
mastectomy	64	Bressler (1956)
	34	Weinstein *et al.* (1964)

et al. point out most clearly, however, the evidence against this explanation. They suggest that fantasies are never so consistent as to be universally found among any class of persons, and that a painful, distorted fantasy does not seem very gratifying in terms of wish fulfillment. More conclusively, however, Weinstein, *et al.* have found in their own research that the values attached to various body parts bear little relationship to the incidence of phantoms for that part.

The *peripheral* theory of phantoms, on the other hand, ascribes their occurrence to changes in sensitivity of the stump following amputation, principally by the irritation of nerve endings by nerve destruction and scar tissue. Although studies have found increased tactile sensitivity in comparison to the contralateral normal limb, this has not been sufficient to establish the theory. Alternatively, Weinstein, *et al.* offer the suggestion that, as demonstrated in neurophysiological studies, the result may be due to the removal of the inhibitory influence of the distal area of the limb rather than denervation supersensitivity. "It is thus conceivable that the amputation of a distal part removes a region which has potentially inhibiting possibilities upon the more proximal; amputation may therefore result in the greater sensitivity of the stump" (p. 6). These investigators have extended earlier findings in that they have demonstrated that stump sensitivity in size discrimination, point localization, and pressure sensation are increased over the same region of the normal limb. While there are changes in perceptual threshold after amputation, the change may be central rather than peripheral. The peripheral theory also is at a serious disadvantage in explaining the existence and persistence of phantoms with deafferentation and under spinal anesthesia.

A *central* theory of phantom perception has been proposed by both Simmel and Weinstein, *et al.,* the most active researchers in this area, which is closely aligned to "body-image" and its supposed neural substrates. It is equally encouraging that research in this connection may also serve to clarify body-image. Basically, the central theory assumes that the somatosensory cortical representation of the body is the genetic neural framework of the body-image, and also the source of phantom perceptions. Cortical projection of somatic afferents is, in general, organized contralaterally with greater area assigned to the distal body parts—the feet, hands, and facial areas having greatest sensory representation. Critical to the support of the central theory is the degree to which cortical representation and phantom perceptions correspond.

Weinstein, *et al.* have found in their studies of the phantom perceptions of paraplegic persons that there is indeed a significcant correlation between cortical somatosensory representation and the incidence of phantom perceptions. They conclude, "Our findings, thus far, support the theory that the phantom has its origin in the sensory homunculus of the cerebral cortex, and that therefore the phantom and its various attributes can be explained either by some basic somatosensory mechanism or by the interaction of this mechanism with other neurophysiological processes" (p. 71). Previous clinical observations of the abolition of phantom perceptions with cortical lesions also would seem to support this theory, but Weinstein, *et al.* were not able to obtain consistent confirmation of this with fourteen cases who presented cerebrovascular accidents *after* having had amputations. Apparently, strokes in 26 persons *prior* to their amputations did not prevent the occurrence of phantom perceptions. Nevertheless, Weinstein, *et al.* have interpreted their cases as tentatively supporting the observation that contralateral cerebral lesions tend to abolish phantom perceptions while ipsilateral lesions do not.

Additional findings which tend to support the central theory are derived from the patterning of sensory experiences prior to amputation. Simmel reports that the phantoms of deformed limbs are perceived as deformed following amputation, and that the incidence depends upon the degree of sensation presurgically. Furthermore, the phantoms of amputated painful or paralyzed limbs lack "voluntary motion." Weinstein, *et al.* report that phantoms resulting from amputated congenitally deformed or aplasic limbs always conform to the deformity, never an intact limb.

Interesting also in regard to the central theory of phantom perception is the observation of the gradual disappearance of the phantom and that of telescoping. In general, Simmel points out, the gradual disappearance of the phantom proceeds from the proximal to distal parts, i.e., those with the least somatosensory cortical representation disappear first. Likewise, the telescoped phantom preserves the perception of the distal parts, such as toes, which may be perceived as attached directly to the stump. Weiss (1963) has recently called attention to the similarity of telescoped phantom limbs to phocomelia, stating, "In phocomelia, the natural distal limb progresses minimally from its proximal position. In phantom telescoping, the image of the distal part regresses to an earlier embryological position" (p. 1053). Visual factors should be mentioned at this point since both Simmel and Weinstein, *et al.* indicate that it is the visual presence of the extremities which prevents telescoping of the phantom perceptions of paraplegics. Maturational factors, too, are thought to be of significance. Simmel (1962) has found a progressive increase in the incidence of phantom perceptions following amputation from two years to eight years of age. According to Simmel's data, 45% of amputations occurring before the age of four years result in phantoms, 75% up to age eight, and 100% thereafter.

Although the central theory seems at this time to be the most promising in terms of accommodating the research on phantom perceptions, it is not yet possible to say how this might occur. Simmel's assumption is that, "The lost part continues to be represented in the schema and manifests itself experientially as the phantom" (p. 345). The perception arises from the loss of kinesthetic input and the body schema cannot change rapdily enough to accommodate sudden physical alteration. This does not answer the question of the stimulus or energy which enables the phantom to persist, especially in so many variations.

It seems that perhaps these perceptions occur not simply because the lost part of function is still present and perpetuated in the somatosensory cortex, but because as a functional unit registering kinesthetic and other types of sensory input it was an element of many percepts and patterns of response. Any stimulus pattern which serves to activate percepts and response patterns in which the lost function has been an element might produce "awareness," although illusory. Simmel has reluctantly suggested that perhaps the phantom itself becomes incorporated into the body-image. This is not out of the realm of possibility, but it may also be that somatosensory experience and body perception is reorganized and modified gradually to reflect the changed patterns of input and modes of response. Undoubtedly, peripheral sensations will somehow be found to contribute to the ultimate explanation.

The effect of phantom perceptions upon such outcomes as physical improvement, prosthetic training and the like in rehabilitation is no more certain than the effects of bodily perceptions in general. The general feeling seems to be, however, that the phantom's persistence inhibits progress. In spinal cord injuries, for example, phantoms are interpreted as often maintaining unfounded hope for recovery of function and lead to indifference and lack of cooperation in treatment. Of course it is frequently stated that phantoms, if not produced by, are invariably a manifestation of emotional disturbance and impede the patient's progress in rehabilitation. Such negative effects have not been supported by the research to date.

SENSORY COMPENSATION

An aspect of perception that is of very fundamental significance in rehabilitation, but one which typically receives only very specialized attention by those working with deafness and blindness, is that of sensory compensation. The activity of remaining receptor systems and resulting changes in perceptual processes when sensory losses occur is much more pervasive than this, if we consider the very likely possibility that the disruption of any sensory input leads to changes in remaining systems and in the central regulating process. As a generalization, the historical opinion has been that there is equipotentiality among receptor systems so that lost functions can, in part at least, be compensated for by intact systems. In the case of blindness, for example, the tactile and auditory systems have been assumed to take over the individual's transactions with his environment; while for the deaf, the visual and tactile systems assume the increased load. It is an obvious necessity that the deaf or blind person must utilize his remaining receptor systems to a much greater extent to carry on the activities of learning, perception, and communication. How adequately this may be done is still open to question. Furthermore, we should wish to know what occurs in instances of deafferentation such as in spinal cord injuries, amputations or as a result of stroke or peripheral nerve injuries.

Doubtlessly, the loss of any sensory system imposes limitations, but some feel that this depends upon the system affected. Ramsdell (1961) points out that the deaf may compensate for their loss to some extent through the visual system, but further states that, "Because a blind man must also substitute one sense for another, blindness and deafness are popularly classed together" (p. 461). Claiming this to be a superficial comparison, Ramsdell remarks, "The tendency to evaluate the effects of deafness in the terms used for blindness has retarded an understanding of the psychology of the deafened" (p. 461). To this point Pauls (1961) states, "Contrary to popular opinion, the man who is deaf or blind does not miraculously acquire a 'supersense' to compensate for his particular handicap. Instead, he must learn to utilize to the utmost what he has left to work with. It is a shift of attention that enables him to work seeming miracles" (p. 354).

It seems most likely that the concept of "attention" which was briefly mentioned by Pauls is the key to the whole subject of residual sensory activity. In recent years, the mechanisms of attention have been the subject of much interest among neurophysiologists who have produced evidence to demonstrate that all receptor systems are monitored and controlled by the central regulating (attention regulating) systems of the brain stem and thalamus. The central nervous system is thereby shown not to be the passive recipient and analyzer of any and all information that falls upon the senses but is capable of controlling its own input as well as the processing of the information and programming of responses. Furthermore, the central regulating mechanisms exert a very *selective* control over receptor activity performing a switching as well as a monitoring function which is absolutely necessary for attention or the focusing of attention. By this means, the transmission and processing of information through certain sensory channels may be facilitated while at the same time inhibiting the activity of other channels. A reasonable hypothesis, therefore, would follow that when a sensory system is disrupted or lost completely the central regulating mechanisms are able to adjust residual sensory activity accordingly and able to shift "attention" through other systems. This is an hypothesis that is readily subject to test by methods available for studying sensory systems electrophysiologically. Zemtzova, Novikova, Paramonova, and Sokolov (1965) have, however, supplied contrary observations in that they have found the orienting reflex or alerting response to auditory stimulus that is characteristic of attention to habituate more quickly in blind persons than in persons with normal vision.

The behavioral evidence, however, has been conflicting. Regarding residual sensory activity with blindness, Axelrod (1959) admits that while there are possibilities for the assumption of compensation there is even more evidence to the contrary. Axelrod suggests that no compensatory activity occurs beyond that of normal subjects on tactile and auditory tasks and that the tactile thresholds of blind subjects may, in fact, be raised. Other investigators have also recently shown that the disruption of a sensory system is accompanied by difficulties in information processing in the remaining systems (Myklebust, 1964; Sterritt & Camp & Lipman, 1966; Myklebust & Brutten, 1953). It may be, therefore, that the elimination of a sensory system disrupts the integration of residual sensory functioning, particularly when occurring at an early stage of perceptual development.

The work of Soviet neurophysiologists and psychologists in residual sensory activity has recently been summarized in relation to hearing loss by Morkovin (1961) who makes the interpretation that, "The compensatory process, effectively developed, involves the entire organism; growth in auditory discrimination, in sensory substitution, in personality adjustment. According to Soviet neurophysiologists, this process may transform the functional pattern of the central nervous system and may change its level of excitability and lability'' (p. 360). The study of compensatory sensory activity in the Soviet Union has been based upon orienting responses and conditioning "attention" in intact sensory systems. Recent investigators, Zemtzova, Kulagin, and Novikova (1962), have studied the cortical activity of blind persons and have concluded, "The change in the sensory systems after onset of blindness is not limited to the change of some isolated functions but involves the whole central nervous system. The development of processes of compensation evokes a change of the type of intra-analyzer connections and mechanisms of cortical regulation. In the absence of vision, the mechanisms of cortical regulation are based on the extension of the use of hearing, tactile, motor, and other systems of sensory analysis (safe analyzers) which have a compensatory function in blindness" (p. 74). Zemtzova, Kulagin, and Novikova have produced evidence which they interpret as showing not only a lowering of cortical excitability in the blind, but at the same time disinhibition of subcortical structures. They have concluded that, "This increase of the excitation level in subcortical structures serves as one of the sources of compensatory excitation of the cortex and explains several specific features of vegetative reactions in the blind" (p. 76). A relevant study in this country by Mark and Hardy (1958) partially substantiates lowered cortical excitability but does not illuminate residual sensory activity in other modalities.

Thus, there is some evidence that adjustments in the central regulating process occur as a result of sensory loss, explaining the findings of decreased peripheral sensitivity in remaining sensory systems. Reduced cortical excitability leads to perceptual disruption. Disinhibition, or increased subcortical excitability, produces disruption in the selection and processing of sensory information and the shifting of attention.

Less extreme samples of sensory loss have not produced these same results. In amputations, for example, investigations by Teuber, Krieger, and Bender (1949) and Weinstein, *et al.* have demonstrated increased peripheral tactile sensitivity of the stump, which the latter interpret to be the result of the removal of inhibiting distal input. Weinstein, *et al.* conclude that these findings are consistent with two hypotheses: "The first proposes that increased sensitivity of the stump results from a reduction of background levels of nervous activity, in contrast to the undiminished level of the contralateral side. The second proposes that the greater sensitivity of the stump derives from the greater 'availability' of cortex. That is, sensory cortex not serving distal portions of the limb is available to the more proximal regions, thereby enhancing the sensitivity of the stump" (p. 67).

It is difficult to interpret the evidence accumulated thus far with any degree of clarity. However, it seems that compensation, if such occurs at all, is a matter of the shifting of attention centrally rather than changes in the sensitivity of specific receptors. The loss of major sensory input apparently has a disruptive effect upon perception and information processing in general; but it may be, at least in some systems, that a partial restriction of input increases the sensitivity of proximal structures having related innervation. This is one of the most neglected areas of psychological research in physical disability, even though considerable research has been accomplished recently in regard to the perceptual and cognitive functions of the deaf (Furth, 1966).

The systematic application of psychological theories of perception has been very slow in rehabilitation fields. Perhaps one reason is that we have been preoccupied with observable defects and functional limitations and their correction rather than underlying processes and explanations. The following section summarizes relatively recent perceptual theories which seem to hold a special relevance for physical disability and rehabilitation.

APPLICABLE PERCEPTUAL THEORIES

Because we are concerned about structural and functional limitations and changes, it is necessary to seek perceptual theories and research which give attention to motor as well as sensory elements of perceptual experience. This automatically makes our task relatively brief since perceptual theories have involved themselves almost entirely with sensory phenomena. A notable exception is the "Sensory-Tonic" Theory of Werner and Wapner (1952); the central concept of their theory being that of an interaction between sensory and motor processes in perception.

Sensory-Tonic Theory

Werner and Wapner have emphasized in their research and theoretical work that the "input" in human experience is *never* into a static system but into a system which is already organized in some particular manner. Hence, the sensory-tonic states of the organism, or cognitive and postural adjustments, are the determinants of perceptual experience. According to theory, either sensory or muscular changes affect this sensory-tonic state and cause it to fluctuate, creating changes in perceptual experience which are independent of external events or stimulus conditions. Perceptual experience would then be a function of how the stimulus input is integrated with the existing sensory-tonic state. We could go even farther to say that the "sensory-tonic state" of the organism determines, in a selective way, what stimulus events become inputs; the neurophysiological basis of selective attention and stimulus attenuation having been amply demonstrated by numerous recent investigators.

Werner, Wapner, and their associates have generated a considerable amount of research to support their point of view. In the perception of motion, for example, it has been found that during the perception of illusory movement, under experimental conditions, physical movements (body rotation, eye movements, etc.) ceased. During actual body movement, the perception of illusory motion ceased. These experiments also showed that restricting the voluntary movement of subjects produced increased perceived illusory movement. From such information it has been concluded that there is an interaction between organismic states and stimulus events, and that "sensory-tonic" adjustments have a definite influence upon perceptual experience. Likewise, in the perception of verticality, which is normally somewhat inaccurate, it has been demonstrated that unilateral stimulation of several sorts would cause the subject to perceive the vertical to be displaced in a direction *opposite* the side of stimulation. Similar results have been obtained by tilting the body, unsupported tilting of the body producing a greater effect upon the perceived vertical than supported tilting. This would strongly suggest that altering the sensory-tonic state of the organism produced a definite modification of perceptual experience independent of objective stimulus events. It seems legitimate, therefore, to consider that the existing sensory and motor adjustments of the organism do influence perceptual experience in a very direct manner.

There have been several perceptual investigations, primarily concerning spatial perception in hemiparesis, which have applied the theory and experimental procedures of Werner and Wapner. A number of these studies have concerned themselves particularly with disturbances in the perception of verticality in hemiplegic persons, although other aspects of spatial perception have received attention. Bruell, Peszcynski, and Albee (1956) in their initial report summarized their thinking as follows: "We hypothesize that, if short-lived states of asymmetrical tonus lead to temporary disturbances of space perception, hemiplegic patients who have a permanently asymmetrical distribution of tonus should show permanent disturbances of space perception" (p. 677).

The findings of studies by Bruell, Peszcynski, and Albee (1956) and Bruell, Peszcynski, and Volk (1957) confirmed the existence of distorted spatial perception in hemiplegic patients and provided some interesting preliminary conclusions in regard to the perception of verticality. The first series of 10 left and 7 right hemiplegic patients were compared to normal college students and age-matched controls on the perception of a luminous rod in a dark room. It was found that the hemiplegic subjects showed a significant degree of distortion in the perception of the vertical which was not apparently related to the side affected. There was little difference in the performance of left or right hemiplegic subjects, but they showed as a group considerably greater variability in performance than controls. The preliminary report of Bruell, Peszcynski, and Albee (1956) concluded, "Subjects with hemiplegia showed in exaggerated form what was present to a lesser degree in the two control groups" (p. 678).

A subsequent report by Bruell, Peszcynski, and Volk (1957) confirmed their previous results. In this case a rod and frame apparatus was used with 10 left and 10 right hemiplegic persons and 20 normal controls. Performance was highly consistent for individual control subjects, but again the hemiplegic group showed greater variability in performance.

Other investigations stressing the importance of perceptual processes in motor learning have also been reported for hemiplegic patients. Brich, Proctor, Bortner, and Lowenthal (1960 a,b) have investigated the perception of vertical, horizontal, and median planes in hemiplegic patients. However, contrary to previous reports, hemiplegic patients displaced verticality *toward* the affected side, i.e., left hemiplegics counterclockwise and right hemiplegics clockwise. Conditions were comparable to the studies of Bruell, *et al.* (1956) in that the luminous rod alone was employed in darkness. Under these conditions, 22 right and 21 left hemiplegic subjects demonstrated significant distortion of vertical perception as compared to controls and were also more variable in performance. The perception of the horizontal position of a rod in darkness clearly indicated the left hemiplegic group to manifest greater distortion (Birch, *et al.,* 1960 a). When tested under conditions of normal room illumination, allowing the use of other spatial cues, distortion was greatly reduced on both vertical and horizontal planes among hemiplegic subjects who nevertheless still showed a degree of perceptual dysfunction. The perception of the median plane for 14 right and 11 left hemiplegics was found to show a characteristic displacement toward the affected side, once again to a lesser degree under normal illuminations (Birch, *et al.,* 1960 b). In fact, whereas in darkness normal controls and left hemiplegic subjects judged the midline to the left, this was reversed under illumination so that all three groups displaced their perception of the median plane to the right of the objective midline.

We have in these two sets of investigations (Bruell, *et al.,* 1956, 1957; Birch, *et al.,* 1960 a,b) still some uncertainty in regard to the direction of displacement of the vertical by hemiplegic patients. This is important to the theory presently under consideration. From the theory and experimental results of Werner and Wapner based upon normal perceptual processes we would expect that displacement would be *toward* the paretic side, i.e., toward the side of least sensory input in the unbalanced system, the disequilibrium having been created by the partial or complete loss of kinesthetic and tactual sensation on the paretic side. Bruell, *et al.* (1956, 1957) found no consistent differences in their hemiplegic subjects. Birch *et al.* (1960 a,b), on the other hand, found displacement in the predicted direction on both vertical and median plane judgments. Hulicka and Beckenstein (1961) have added findings of displacement of vertical perception *opposite* the paretic side.

The incongruence of directional findings for hemiplegic subjects does not, however, discount Werner and Wapner's Sensory-Tonic theory of perception. With hemiplegia we not only have asymmetrical sensation and motor imbalance but central perceptual changes as well, which very well could have confounded these results. Birch, Belmont, Reilly, and Belmont (1962) have recently attempted to counteract the state of disequilibrium in hemiplegia and its effects upon the perception of verticality. Their study involving 20 left hemiplegic patients and 18 non-brain damaged controls tested vertical perception in the usual way, but later added a ten-pound weight to one or the other shoulder of their subjects. Judgment improved slightly with added somesthetic stimulation to the paretic side, but in general no significant change in mean constant errors was produced by the added weight.

An especially interesting study along the sensory-tonic lines has recently been reported by Comalli (1966) involving a comparison of verticality judgments of 13 left and 13 right above-the-knee amputees. Comalli's results were that the perception of the vertical was significantly displaced *opposite* the side of the amputation. He has inferred a counteractive force in the direction opposite the side of amputation and has suggested that differences in his results and those for hemiplegic patients as being due to brain damage in hemiplegia, adjustment to prosthesis in amputation, or both.

In reconciling the apparent differences in experimental results, it should be recognized that in dealing with limb amputation and hemiplegia we are dealing with contrary states of disequilibrium. In hemiplegia there is a partial or complete unilateral loss of sensitivity and motor control, whereas in amputation the sensitivity of the stump is actually increased over the contralateral normal limb (Weinstein, *et al.*), quite probably with added vivid or even painful phantom sensations. Therefore, if perception is compensated *toward* the side of *reduced* input, this would be toward the paretic side in hemiplegia and toward the contralateral normal limb in amputation. I believe this interpretation is consistent with Werner and Wapner's general theoretical assumption that increased stimulation on one side of the body leads to counteractive or balancing forces toward the opposite side in order to restore organismic equilibrium. This is manifest in spatial perception in changing the object's position in space in a direction opposite the side of increased stimulation, clearly, toward the side of reduced stimulation. The flow of "energy" would, therefore, seem to be from positive to negative (see Fig. 2).

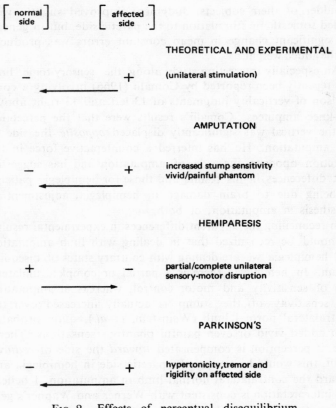

FIG. 2. Effects of perceptual disequilibrium.

Day and Wade (1966) have recently demonstrated a displacement in perceived vertical under conditions of prolonged head-tilting. In their normal subjects, who held their heads tilted to one side or the other for two to three minutes, the direction of displacement was opposite the direction of head-tilt when judgments were made after returning the head to an "upright" position. It was noted, however, that compensatory inclination of the head was present and perceived by these subjects in the opposite direction when the head was returned to an "upright position." Displacement was in the same direction of head-tilt when judgments were made with the head still in the tilted position. Previous neurophysiological research has shown that neuromuscular mechanisms of the neck are responsible. Cohen (1961) anesthetized the dorsal roots of C1, 2, 3 bilaterally in ten monkeys and produced defects in balance, orientation, and motor coordination similar to effects of bilateral labyrinthectomy reported earlier by other workers.

Apparently these results stem from sensory-tonic adjustments involving proprioceptors of the neck. Returning the head to an apparent upright position after prolonged tilting creates compensatory neuromuscular activity toward the opposite side in order to balance that produced by tilting. In a tilted position neuromuscular adjustments seem to be against the tilt. Hence, in spatial perception, displacement is toward the direction of reduced input in the unbalanced system.

It seems completely justifiable to assume that the changes of perception resulting from sensory-motor involvement have important implications in the management and progress of hemiplegic patients. Several recent studies have been accomplished concerning the question, but there has been little consistency in their findings. Van Buskirk and Webster (1955) have attempted to clarify the relationship of sensory deficit to recovery of function and rehabilitation progress in studying 35 male hemiplegic patients through pain and vibratory sensitivity and tactile discrimination. A high rate of impairment in all three perceptual factors was found. Those patients with intact sensitivity were hospitalized for a shorter period of time with about one-half of their number achieving a "satisfactory rehabilitation result." Those who later recovered sensation were hospitalized somewhat longer, but all apparently attained a "satisfactory rehabilitation result." Patients who failed to recover sensation stayed very much longer in the hospital, and for the majority treatment was reported to have ended with poor results.

In terms of spatial perception, Bruell, Peszczynski, and Volk (1957) found, when they divided their 20 hemiplegic subjects into categories of "good walkers," "poor walkers," and wheelchair patients, that there was a general relationship between distortion in verticality percepton and ambulation. Whether these patients' perception of the vertical determined their ability to ambulate or whether their mobility and body orientation determined their perceptual organization was not explained.

A similar study of 41 male patients reported by Hulicka and Beckenstein (1961) included 15 hemiplegics unable to walk, 11 who were walking, and 15 with no CNS disorder. All were tested using the rod alone, and rod and frame apparatus with the result that all hemiplegic patients made greater errors, but non-walkers were poorest. Two possible explanations were recognized—that those hemiplegic patients who were able to walk perceived the vertical more accurately because of increased environmental contact, or successful ambulation depends on accurate vertical perception.

Two somewhat more generalized studies of the relation of spatial perception to rehabilitation outcomes may also be mentioned, both of which have used standardized tests of visual perceptual organization. Lorenze and Cancko (1962) studied a group of 41 hemiplegic patients, 16 right and 25 left hemiplegics, to determine the relationship between perceptual dysfunction and success in relearning activities of daily living. Of the total group, 9 patients failed to achieve independence in dressing and 3 in self-grooming. All of these patients were reported to have obtained significantly lower scores on the type of tests given (combined total weighted score on Block Design and Object Assembly tests). Lorenze and Cancko concluded that success in retraining in activities of daily living is a function of the degree of visual perceptual distortion, but this was not conclusively demonstrated.

Rosenthal, Pearson, Medenica, Manaster, and Smith (1965) have also investigated this relationship among 49 left hemiplegic patients who were given standardized perceptual tests as well as having been evaluated within 48 hours of admission in performance of self-care activities. Reevaluation preceded discharge. This research found no significant relationship between visual perceptual dysfunction and the degree of improvement in rehabilitation in terms of self-care activities of daily living. Rosenthal, *et al.* have suggested that the failure of their study to confirm such a well-accepted relationship probably lies in their methodology and the measurement devices used.

Thus far we have encountered mostly discouraging results in attempting to relate perceptual factors to physical improvement or rehabilitation progress. Neither body-image "distortions," phantom perceptions, or visual-spatial distortions such as in the displacement of perceived vertical have unquestionably been shown to have a bearing upon the question. It may well be that human beings are capable of adapting, even with central nervous system damage, to fairly severe conditions of perceptual disruption and that the capacity to adapt to changed input patterns is the really significant variable with which we should be concerned. Some enlightenment of the issues will be found in the discussion to follow concerning a very promising theoretical and experimental framework derived by Karl U. Smith.

Neurogeometric Theory

Smith and Henry (1966) have outlined for us not only a most intriguing theory of perception and the organization of human behavior, but also a systematic approach to treatment and even equipment design in physical rehabilitation. This theory, like the Sensory-Tonic Theory of Werner and Wapner (1952), emphasizes the interaction and inseparability of sensory and motor components in perception and has been concisely summarized by Smith and Henry as follows:

> We can summarize the concept of human motions as self-governed action mechanisms in the following concrete way. In functioning as closed-loop mechanisms, given sectors of the body are guided by self-generated stimulus feedback patterns. The body does not respond to chance external stimuli, but to feedback stimuli generated and regulated by specialized movement. Each movement creates directional space displacements in the feedback patterns, which are detected by nerve cells and used to control the form and timing of further motions. Learning involves the establishment of direction-specificity and dendrite specificity of neuron detectors as a change in the orientation of molecular elements of the cells related to the dendritic structure. Memory is the retention of such directional specificity and is a mode of time control and perception that consists of a neural record of patterns and combinations of movements. This record also is used to extrapolate feedforward control over movements to be made in the immediate future. That is, performance is not guided by immediate sensory feedback alone, but also by the persisting memory trace of past movement feedback and by related anticipatory prediction of response which we call feedforward control of motion (p. 65-6).

Smith (1961 a,b) has outlined in several theoretical and experimental articles a cybernetic theory of perception and behavior which is based upon the conception of the human organism as a self-regulating, self-correcting system. Human perception, learning, and motivation are, in this approach, activities intrinsically organized and controlled and not directly dependent upon extrinsic stimulation or influence. Physiological impairments and changes would be found to effect these intrinsic organizing and controlling actions.

It is fundamental to the theory that all human functions or processes, physiological or psychological, are under the same type of regulation and control. The theory is entirely functional in that all behavior has the unitary purpose of supporting the self-regulatory systems. Perception, or any other aspect of behavior, cannot then be considered to be a response to externally determined events, but is a highly specialized activity designed to maintain the integration and functioning of all organismic activities within definitely programmed limits of tolerance or error. Smith and Henry have also made other assumptions concerning the self-regulating processes of behavior that require elaboration, especially in relation to feedback control and disruptions of feedback.

Basically, feedback is a response triggered by *stimulus differences* on sensor surfaces constantly being generated by the organism itself. The more critical differences to be taken into account are displacements occurring in sensory input information, either spatially or temporally, with unusual feedback displacements being produced by physical injuries. The theory hypothesizes three levels of feedback control (even the simplest actions requiring simultaneous coordinated control of receptor action) postural, transport, and manipulative (articulate) movement systems in conjunction with autonomic adjustment. In every activity, the efficacy of behavior depends upon adequate feedback from the *focus of action* so that behavior regulation is not only response specific but topologically specific. Feedback, in the Neurogeometric Theory, comes in three forms. They are *reactive*, that generated by bodily movement; *instrumental*, derived from the actions of tools or instruments and objects manipulated; and *operational*, generated by the effects of operations on the environment. But feedback is also subject to various "social transformations" from social interaction and social "tracking" (imitation, group action, etc.). In fact, one of the most interesting features of this theory is what Smith and Henry call "yoked feedback control" in which one person supplies feedback by means of which the other controls his activity. This is primarily a somesthetic control, although other receptor systems are doubtlessly involved as would be found operative in dancing or sexual intercourse, for example.

Smith's research in support of this theory has been quite extensive (see Smith, 1961 a,b) and has dealt mainly with delays and displacements of feedback in the visual and auditory systems which are quite reliable in the capacity to produce behavioral disruptions particularly in skilled performances (see Figs. 3 and 4). The implications of the Neurogeometric Theory and supporting research for all aspects of treatment and rehabilitation are of potentially far-reaching significance and hopefully will be more fully investigated.

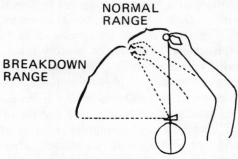

NORMAL
RANGE

BREAKDOWN
RANGE

FIG. 3. The three basic assumptions of neurophysiological regulation of motion in Neurogeometric Theory. These are: 1) every movement has a "normal range" of space displacement in which the motion can be performed; 2) beyond this limited normal range geometric displacement between the receptor-motor system causes disturbance or disorganization of the movement; and 3) the degree of disturbance and rate and level of learning within this breakdown range will be a function of the relative magnitude of the displacement. (From Smith, Gould & Wargo, 1964.)

In principle, at least, the implications of this theory are fairly obvious. Any physiological impairment or change which interferes with the mechanisms of feedback, therefore, disrupts the effective organization and control of behavior. This would be true whether the impairment be primarily sensory in nature (reduced, absent or distorted input), a matter of motor control (limitation of postural, transport or articulate action), or damage to the central nervous system mechanisms necessary for the selection, processing and integration of feedback.

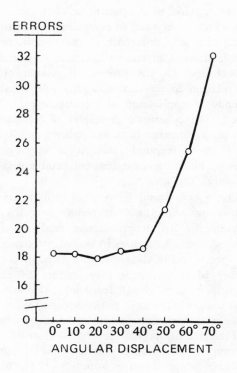

Fig. 4. Angular displacement and errors in performance. (From Gould & Smith, 1963.)

The objective of any rehabilitation effort, regardless of technology, would, therefore, be to restore maximum self-regulatory control to each individual. The objective would involve procedures designed to retrain mechanisms or systems of control, to use residual sources of feedback or substitute feedback, and to correct or reduce the behavioral and physiological effects of displacements. At a more complex behavioral level, vocational rehabilitation would serve the purpose of restoring personal-social-economic independence which is a most important aspect of self-regulation and control. Therefore, with the point of view in mind of the patient or client as a self-regulatory system which is in need of correction or repair, it should be clear that the only difference in the various rehabilitation fields or professions is in technology, not in principle.

As a conclusion to the present discussion of perceptual theories in relation to physical disability and rehabilitation, a possible avenue of application of Neurogeometric Theory may be mentioned. The cybernetic principles of feedback and control are of vital significance in these applications. Reference will be made to the perceptual research of investigators in the chronic disease, but to some extent correctable disability associated with, parkinsonism.

Dinnerstein, Frigyesi and Lowenthal (1962) have suggested that parkinsonian symptoms of tremor, rigidity, and hypokinesis may be due to proprioceptive feedback delays. They point to the fact that disruptions in skilled patterned movements such as in speech and in visual-motor acts have been produced by a number of independent investigators by the temporal delay of auditory and visual feedback. Dinnerstein, *et al.* propose that the oscillations in parkinsonian tremor are simply exaggerations of normal tremor rhythms and may be compared to those of electromechanical feedback systems. They have stated, "Normally, these tremor movements are almost imperceptible because proprioceptive impulses, the afferent consequences of a muscle contraction, arouse antagonistic muscles which oppose the tendency to movement or which return the limb to its orginal starting position. If the occurrence of transmission of the proprioceptive impulses were excessively delayed, the initial automatic movement would be larger because the antagonistic muscle contraction would be delayed. The resulting sequence of new delayed proprioceptive impulses and the inevitably delayed and prolonged compensating muscle contractions would produce oscillating movement" (p. 669). Rigidity and hypokinesis, or slowing of behavior, would likewise be explained by abnormal delays in transmission of proprioceptive impulses, these investigators having made the assumption that these complex motor symptoms, "do not necessarily indicate a malfunction of specific motor control center or disruption of pathways" (Dinnerstein, *et al.,* p.670).

Clinically, the proposed explanation may shed some light on paradoxical behavior of parkinsonian patients. It has been observed in their laboratory by Dinnerstein, *et al.* that patients who cannot walk may be able to march or dance to music, while patients who cannot feed themselves may be able to catch a ball. Under such conditions, "An external stimulus provided an alternative to proprioception" (p. 673). Experimentally, Dinnerstein, *et al.* have found that parkinsonian patients differ from normal and age-matched controls in perceptual speeds, Parkinson patients showing greater delays in touch and audition but greater speeds in vision, delays being relieved somewhat with chemotherapy (see Fig. 5). A subsequent study has confirmed excessive proprioceptive delays (Dinnerstein, Lowenthal, Blake & Mallin, 1964). Levita & Riklan (1965) have found that, at least in terms of visual perceptual speeds, subcortical surgery exaggerates the delays during the immediate postoperative period. However, "Follow-up data indicate that surgically imposed subcortical lesions do not affect adversely the temporal aspects of perceptual performance" (p. 298).

It is worthwhile mentioning at this point some studies by Proctor, Riklan, Cooper, and Teuber (1964) concerning the perception of verticality by Parkinson patients. Their subjects

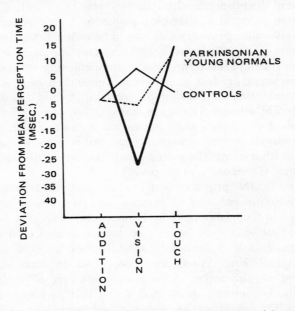

Fig. 5.   Relative speeds of perception in audition, vision and touch for parkinsonian patients, for a control group of aged non-neurological patients, and for a group of young normals. There were 12 *Ss* in each group. The difference in perception speed pattern, between the parkinsonian group and the control group was significant with $p < .02$. (From Dinnerstein, Frigyesi & Lowenthal, 1962.)

were thirty-eight patients of whom sixteen had maximal involvement on the left and twenty-two on the right side. Patients were tested under a variety of conditions, both pre- and postoperatively. All patients had chemothalamectomy and were tested two weeks and five months later. On the visual vertical (luminous rod) these patients were found to displace the vertical *opposite* the involved side, in comparison to other findings that hemiplegics displace *toward* and unilateral amputees *opposite* their affected side. Surgery, which relieved patient's motor symptoms, did not correct the visual-spatial distortion which was in fact exaggerated immediately post-operatively but had stabilized within five months.

Some promising avenues of psychological research in physical disability could well be opened through attention to perceptual functions such as feedback and its disruption, as the illustrative work of Dinnerstein, *et al.* and others are suggesting. Developments in such analyses are to be found in Smith, Ansell, and Smith (1963) and Smith, Gould, and Wargo (1964) which would seem to hold potential significance to rehabilitation of the physically disabled. In this, as in other aspects of behavior to be discussed in the following chapter, psychological research in physical disability and rehabilitation can best contribute by illuminating the processes of behavior regulation and control, the disruptions occurring as a result of chronic illness and permanent physiological impairments or changes, and the means of restoring or manipulating systems of behavior organization.

References

Abercrombie, M. & Tyson, M. Body image and Draw-A-Man test in cerebral palsy. *Develmt. Med. Child Neurol.*, 1966, **8**, 9-15.

Axelrod, S. Effects of early blindness: Performance of blind and sighted children on tactile and auditory tasks. 1959, *Amer. Found. Blind, Res. Monogr. No. 7.*

Barker, R., Wright, B. & Gonick, M. *Adjustment to Physical Handicap and Illness; A Survey of the Social Psychology of Physique and Disability.* 1946, Soc. Sci. Res. Council, New York.

Birch, H., Belmont, I., Reilly, T. & Belmont, L. Somesthetic influences on perception of visual verticality in hemiplegia. *Arch. PM&R*, 1962, **43**, 556-60.

Birch, H., Proctor, F., Bortner, M. & Lowenthal, M. Perception in Hemiplegia: I. Judgement of vertical and horizontal by hemiplegic patients. *Arch. PM&R*, 1960, **41**, 19-27.

Birch, H., Proctor, F., Bortner, M. & Lowenthal, M. Perception in Hemiplegia: II. Judgement of the median plane. *Arch. PM&R* 1960, **41**, 71-5.

Bors, E. Phantom limbs of patients with spinal cord injury. *Arch. Neurol. Psychiat.*, 1951, **66**, 610-31.

Bressler, B., Cohen, S. & Magnussen, F. The problem of phantom breast and phantom pain. *J. Nerv. Ment. Dis.*, 1956, **123**, 181-7.

Bruell, J., Peszczynski, M. & Albee, G. Disturbance of perception of verticality in patients with hemiplegia: A preliminary report. *Arch. PM&R*, 1956, **37**, 677-9.

Bruell, J., Peszczynski, M. & Volk, D. Disturbance of perception of verticality in patients with hemiplegia: Second report. *Arch. PM&R*, 1957, **38**, 776-80.

Campbell, E., Bansavage, J., Van Ormer, J. & Dick, E. The psychological and social factors related to successful prosthetic training in juvenile amputees. *Interclinic Inform. Bull.*, 1964, 3, No. 12.

Centers, L. & Centers, R. A comparison of the body-image of amputees and nonamputee children as revealed in figure drawings. *J. Proj. Techs.*, 1963, 27, 258-65.

Cohen, L. Role of eye and neck proprioceptive mechanisms in body orientation and motor coordination. *J. Neurophys.*, 1961, 24, 1-10.

Comalli, P. Effect of unilateral above-the-knee amputation on perception of verticality. *Percept. Mot. Skills*, 1966, 23, 91-6.

Day, R. & Wade, N. Visual spatial after effect from prolonged head-tilt. *Science*, 1966, 154, 1201-02.

Dinnerstein, A., Frigyesi, T. & Lowenthal, M. Delayed feedback as a possible mechanism in parkinsonism. *Percept. Mot. Skills*, 1962, 15, 667-80.

Dinnerstein, A., Lowenthal, M., Blake, G., & Mallin, R. Tactile delay in parkinsonism. *J. Nerv. Ment. Dis.*, 1964, 139, 521-4.

Evans, J. On disturbance of the body-image in paraplegia. *Brain*, 1962, 85, 687-700.

Fink, S. & Shontz, F. Body-image disturbances in chronically ill individuals. *J. Nerv. Ment. Dis.*, 1960, 131, 234-40.

Fisher, S. & Cleveland, S. *Body-Image and Personality.* 1958, Van Nostrand, New York.

Furth, H. *Thinking Without Language: Psychological Implications of Deafness.* 1966, Free Press, New York.

Gould, J. & Smith, K. Angular displacement of visual feedback in motion and learning. *Percept. Mot. Skills*, 1963, 17, 699-710.

128   PHYSICAL DISABILITY AND HUMAN BEHAVIOR

Gregory, R.   Visual illusions. *Sci. Amer.*, 1968, **219**, 66-76.

Haber, W.   Effects of loss of limb on sensory functions. *J. Psychol.*, 1955, **40**, 115-23.

Held, R. & Bauer, J.   Visually guided reaching in infant monkeys after restricted rearing. *Science*, 1967, **155**, 718-20.

Hulicka, I. & Beckenstein, L.   Perception of the vertical by hemiplegic patients. *Amer. J. Phys. Med.*, 1961, **42**, 192-200.

Kuhn, R.   Functional capacity of the isolated human spinal cord. *Brain*, 1950, **73**, 1-51.

Levita, E. & Riklan, M.   Temporal aspects of perceptual functions after surgery of subcortical structures. *J. Psychol.*, 1965, **59**, 295-8.

Livingston, K.   The phantom limb syndrome. *J. Neurosurg.*, 1945, **2**, 251-5.

Lorenze, E. & Cancko, R.   Dysfunction in visual perception with hemiplegia: Its relation to activities of daily living. *Arch. PM&R* 1962, **43**, 514-17.

Mark, H. & Hardy, W.   Orienting reflex disturbances in central auditory or language handicapped children. *J. Sp. Hear. Dis.*, 1958, **23**, 237-42.

Mason, R.   *Internal Perception and Bodily Functioning.* 1961, International Universities Press, New York

Morkovin, B.   Mechanisms of compensation for hearing loss: Theories and research in the Soviet Union. *J. Sp. Hear. Dis.*, 1961, **26**, 359-67.

Myklebust, H.   *The Psychology of Deafness.* 1964, Grune & Stratton, New York.

Myklebust, H. & Brutten, M.   A study of the visual perception of deaf children. *Acta Oto-largng.*, 1953, Suppl. 105.

Ohio Occup. Therapy Assoc. Body-Image. Conference proceedings, 1966. Cleveland, OOTA (mimeo).

Penfield, W. & Jasper, H. *Epilepsy and the Functional Anatomy of the Human Brain.* 1954, Little, Brown, Boston.

Pribram, K. A review of theory in physiological psychology. *Ann. Rev. Psychol.,* 1960, 11, 1-40.

Proctor, F., Riklan, M., Cooper, I. & Teuber, H-L. Judgement of visual and postural vertical by parkinsonian patients. *Neurol.,* 1964, 14, 287-93.

Rogers, C. The organization of personality. *Amer. Psycholgst.,* 1957, 2, 358-68.

Rogers, C. *Client Centered Therapy.* 1951, Houghton-Mifflin, Boston

Rosenthal, A., Pearson, L., Medenica, B., Manaster, A. & Smith, C. Correlation of perceptual factors with rehabilitation of hemiplegic patients. *Arch. PM&R,* 1965, 46, 461-6.

Secord, P. & Jourard, S. Appraisal of body-cathexis: Body cathexis and the self. *J. Consult. Psychol.,* 1953, 17, 343-7.

Shontz, F., Fink, S. & Hallenbeck, C. Chronic physical illness as threat. *Arch. PM&R,* 1960, 41, 143-7.

Shontz, F. Body-Part Size Judgement. 1964, Univ. Kansas, Lawrence. Final Rpt. VRA research project No. 814 (mimeo).

Simmel, M. The reality of phantom sensations. *Soc. Research,* 1962, 29, 337-56.

Smith, K. The geometry of human motion and its neural foundations. I. Perceptual and motor adaptation to displaced vision. *Amer. J. Phys. Med.,* 1961a, 40, 71-87.

Smith, K. The geometry of human motion and its neural foundations. II. Neurogeometric theory and its experimental basis. *Amer. J. Phys. Med.,* 1961b, 40, 109-29.

Smith, K., Ansell, S. & Smith, W.   Sensory feedback analysis in medical research. I. Delayed sensory feedback in behavior and neural functions. *Amer. J. Phys. Med.,* 1963, **42**, 228-61.

Smith, K., Gould, J. & Wargo, L.   Sensory feedback analysis in medical research. II. Spatial organization of neurobehavioral systems. *Amer. J. Phys. Med.,* 1964, **43**, 49-84.

Smith, K. & Henry, J.Cybernetic Foundations of Rehabilitation Science. 1966, Behav. Cybernet. Lab., Univ. Wisc. (mimeo).

Sterritt, G., Camp, B. & Lipman, B.   Effects of early auditory deprivation upon auditory and visual information processing. *Percept. Mot. Skills,* 1966, **23**, 123-30.

Teuber, H-L., Krieger, H. & Bender, M.   Reorganization of sensory function in amputation stumps: Two point discrimination. *Fed. Proc.,* 1949, **8**, 156.

Van Buskirk, C. & Webster, D.   Prognostic value of sensory defect in rehabilitation of hemiplegics. *Neurol.,* 1955, **5**, 407-11.

Wachs, H. & Zaks, M.   Studies of body image in men with spinal cord injury. *J. Nerv. Ment. Dis.,* 1960, **131**, 121-7.

Weinstein, S., Vetter, R. & Sersen, E. Physiological and Experiential Concomitants of the Phantom. 1964, Albert Einstein Coll. Med., New York, Final Rpt. VRA research project No. 427 (mimeo).

Werner, H. & Wapner, S.   Toward a general theory of perception. *Psychol. Rev.,* 1952, **49**, 324-38.

Wright, B.   *Physical Disability: A Psychological Approach.* 1960, Harper, New York.

Zemtzova, M., Kulagin, J. & Novikova, L.   The use of remaining sensory channels (safe analyzers) in compensation of visual function in blindness. *Res. Bull. Amer. Found. Blind,* 1962, **2**, 72-87.

Zemtzova, M., Novikova, L., Paramonova, N. & Sokolov, E. Investigation of the orienting reflex to sound stimuli in blind persons. In *Orienting Reflex and Exploratory Behavior,* 1965, pp. 368-76, Amer. Inst. Biol. Sci., Washington, D.C.

VENABLES, J., DOVESDAY, P., PETERSON, R., LEGROS, G.,
Investigation of the growth of . . . round metal in thin
sections. Rev. Franç. Métall. and Corrosion Métaux, 46,
pp. 385–93 in Metal Finish Biol. Chem. Washington 1964.

Chapter V

MOTIVATION—THE ORGANIZATION AND DIRECTION OF BEHAVIOR

In ORDER to efficiently organize and direct their behavior, people spend a great deal of time selecting and processing appropriate information, making decisions, and assessing the outcomes of their efforts. Miller, Galanter, and Pribram (1960) have expressed a conception of motivation as the formulation and execution of "plans", a plan for the human organism being essentially the same as a program for a computer. Miller, *et al.* have defined the organization of behavior, or more precisely a plan, as, "any hierarchical process in the organism that can control the order in which a sequence of operations is to be performed" (p. 16). Central organizing mechanisms which not only control direction but sequential operations were earlier postulated by Lashley (1948) for even such complex samples of motivated behavior as speech.

More specific applications of such models of motivation are to be found in Atkinson and Feather (1966) who have decribed a theory of decision - making under conditions of risk and motivation in general, which is based on the fundamental hedonistic principle of seeking success and avoiding failure. Other equivalent terms, however, might be substituted for success-failure, such as comfort-pain, approval-rejection, etc. Very briefly, Atkinson and Feather's idea is as follows:

The theory identifies the mainsprings of action as an individual is confronted with the challenge to achieve and the threat of failure that are both present whenever his ability is put to the test and when there is some degree of uncertainty about whether he will succeed or fail. The theory asserts that a person's motive to achieve, his motive to avoid failure, and his expectation of success in some venture strongly influence the character of his motivation as it is expressed in level of aspiration, preference for risk, willingness to put forth effort and to persist in an activity (p. v).

A major part of the theory is that decisions made now are to some extent continuous with those made previously, and that the meaning, value, or utility of the objective plays an important role in motivation. It has been determined, for example, that ordinarily people will choose activities of intermediate uncertainty, rather than very difficult (little likelihood of success) or very easy (very high probability of success), except that for goals of high value there is less tendency to choose more difficult conditions. Persistence is expressed in terms of the continuation of activity under decreased expectation of success with repeated failure. Such models of motivation, however, assume the ability to perform as a preexisting state. For complicated actions, this is a very great assumption and one subject to various inferences as Vroom (1964) has recently pointed out.

Vroom explains that there are three alternative models of the relationship of motivation to performance as represented by the three curves in the following figure. The first is that the level of performance is a constantly increasing function of the amount of motivation (solid line). The second (dots) infers a diminishing return so that increments in motivation are only effective in raising performance up to a certain point. The third model is that usually described as an inverted U function with neither very high nor very low doses of motivation as being effective in maintaining high levels of performance. Vroom's assessment of the evidence available in the psychological research is that most investigators would accept the inverted U function as the most satisfactory model. It has often been inferred that while low motivation yields low returns because of

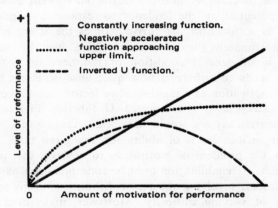

FIG. 6. Hypothetical relationships between amount of motivation and level of performance. (From Vroom, 1964.)

insufficient rewards, interest or involvement in the performance task, very high motivation is usually accompanied by emotional interference which very definitely disrupts response efficiency.

The problem is even more complex than this, however. Vroom reminds us that there is an interaction between motivation and ability which ultimately determines performance level. Vroom suggests the formula:

$$\text{Performance} = \int (\text{Ability} \times \text{Motivation})$$

from which it follows that, "When ability has a low value, increments in motivation will result in smaller increases in performance than when motivation has a high value" (Vroom, 1964, p. 203). The merit of such a model has recently been substantiated by a series of investigations reported by Locke (1965) which were specifically designed to test such an inter- action. The general function reported by Locke was in the form of parallel curves, indicating the multiplicative function of moti- vation. The function reminds one of the old Hullian concept of reaction potential, or the tendency to respond in a particular manner, as a function of "drive" times the strength of the habit. Unfortunately, the definition of "drive" itself by Hull as a non-specific or general condition of the nervous system to which all needs contribute is now quite unsatisfactory, but the notion of motivation as a multiplicative factor seems acceptable.

If we extrapolated the inverted U function in relation to ability, theoretically we would have a distribution of U-shaped curves for various levels of ability for any given task. But to return to the problem of motivation to achieve, the question as we see it in rehabilitation must be conceptualized as a con- tinuous process involving the accomplishment of many separate objectives of varying difficulty. Moreover, many discrete de- cisions have to be made which determine the objectives. The basic concepts of Atkinson and Feather's theory of achieve- ment motivation are thought especially applicable as they have been stated in the following:

> The general approach, of which the theory of achieve- ment motivation is a particular case, considers motivation expressed in the direction, magnitude, and persistence of behavior as a positive function of the strength of motive within the person, the strength of the expectancy of satisfying the motive through some action instrumental to the attainment of a goal or incentive, and the value of the specific goal or incentive that is presented in a given situation (Atkinson & Feather, 1966, p. 64).

It has further been explained that motivation to perform a specific task is positive when the individual has a greater motive to achieve success and negative when the motive to avoid failure is strongest. Greater persistence at a difficult task is associated with the motive to achieve success, whereas if the individual is more motivated to avoid failure, the tendency to persist is weakened. More clearly, the motive to achieve success excites activity which might be expected to produce success, whereas the motive to avoid failure results in a tendency to avoid activities which are expected to lead to failure. But this is an overgeneralization. The theory has led Atkinson and Feather to also speculate about the personality factors which may be involved, and they have described the extreme cases as the "Achievement-oriented personality" and the "Failure-threatened personality" (pp. 368-70).

One of the most important determinants of a person's motivation to perform a task has frequently been shown to be his own subjective estimates of the chances of success or of a favorable outcome of his efforts. The formulations of Atkinson and Feather and others in relation to motivation and decision-making seem especially helpful in considering many types of objectives encountered in vocational and physical rehabilitation. The choices which our patients make, whether obvious to us or covert, and the effort they put forth in attempting to attain their objectives are always of vital and immediate concern, for we believe this motivation in turn to determine the results of rehabilitation programs. We may thus consider the patient's choice of a vocational training goal, an employment opportunity or ambulating with the aid of braces and crutches, as essentially following the same rules. The research and theoretical work in achievement motivation, risk-taking and decision-making have adequately demonstrated that we may view client motivation somewhat more clearly within this sort of framework.

The following model seems at this point most likely. Motivation to pursue an objective and the degree of effort put forth could be represented as being a function of three factors—costs, the probability of a favorable outcome and utility. All three factors are subjective estimates made by clients in regard to a specific activity or objective and probably are independent of actual objective values which they may take.

$$\text{Motivation} = \frac{P(O_S) \times U}{C}$$

Costs represent an estimate of the expense of attempting an activity and may be considered in terms of time, money, physical or mental effort, the endurance of pain or other discomfort, or any other expenditure necessary to performance of a task. The second factor, subjective estimate of the *probability of a successful outcome,* is simply the individual's own personal estimate of his chances of achieving a favorable result of his efforts. *Utility* represents the meaning or value which the client places upon the performance of the task and attainment of the objective. We may conceptualize, then, client motivation in rehabilitation programs as a function of his own estimates of his chances of success times the values he places on attainment of the objective, balanced by his assessment of the costs involved. Rehabilitation counselors can no doubt find many applications of the model to the daily decisions they endeavor to assist clients to make, especially when there are one or more alternative goals from which their clients will choose. The earliest decisions a client will make under these circumstances is whether or not to accept the counselor's offer of assistance. Counselors themselves could, of course, utilize the model by helping the client evaluate the factors of cost, likelihood of success, and utility, although it must be remembered that the final estimates are highly subjective.

It is worthwhile noting, furthermore, that professional decisions too are subject to the same rules. A counselor's decision to accept for services any particular applicant could be predicted by knowing his estimate of the costs of providing the necessary services, his judgment as to the likelihood of a favorable outcome to the case, and the utility he attaches to serving this person, whether moral or practical.

A physical therapist can gauge the motivation of a paraplegic patient, for example, in the laborious task of learning to ambulate efficiently with the aid of mechanical devices by precisely the same means. The patient's assessments of his chances of successful ambulation in relation to the utility or value he attaches to ambulating in this manner could be offset by a very high cost factor. Once we have estimated the level of motivation for a task, however, we still do not have a complete picture of the performance which can be expected. The factor of ability must be considered in relation to level of motivation, both of which, while being relatively consistent for individuals, are subject to fluctuations which affect performance accordingly. Subsequent experience through performance provides the patient with additional information upon which to base his estimates. Both success and failure, it has been suggested, serve to reduce the tendency to continue to perform a specific task, albeit for different reasons.

Before proceeding to some specific research findings it is necessary to clarify one minor point, the distinction between subjective probability of success, a relatively new concept in relation to motivation, and an older psychological concept of "level of aspiration." Level of aspiration has been a favorite means in psychology of quantifying motivation, but suffered from some fundamental inadequacies. Diggory and Morlock (1964) have pointed out that early level of aspiration studies did not deal with the situation in which the immediate goal was to produce within a definite time limit some level of performance which the subject could not readily manipulate. These investigators state, "Level of aspiration may be a valid index of S's feelings of success or failure in a situation where he is free to change his goal from one trial to the next; but if the goal he is trying to achieve is established and maintained by agencies over which he has no control, his estimate of the probability of success is the preferred criterion of his feelings of success or failure" (p. 282). It has concretely been suggested that level of aspiration refers to "What S hopes he can do" and the probability of success to "What S thinks he actually can do."

Now that we have a clearer conception of a few of the principal factors related to motivation to pursue a goal, it will be easier to assess some of the evidence relevant to physical functioning. One may think of situations in rehabilitation in which the patient's goal is prescribed for him, e.g., the efficient use of a prosthesis, ambulation with the aid of leg braces, paid employment, and the like. His performance may be expected to vary with his level of motivation for the tasks involved or, more basically, his estimate of the chances of a successful outcome. Suppose we consider for a moment motivation to be accurately gauged by the magnitude of responses made in the direction of a specific task. There are some very enlightening investigations here that will be helpful, and it is here that research in physiological psychology will be of special significance.

Malmo (1965) has reviewed many studies and has concluded that a number of physiological processes show very dependable variations with subject's task-directed activity. In his review, Malmo states, "To summarize the main findings, progressively rising gradients have been observed in recording skeletal muscle tension (often from muscles not engaged in activity) and in recording cardiovascular and respiratory changes. These gradients have been found to accompany periods of sustained attention, commencing with the onset of the period and rising monotonically to the end, usually with a pronounced drop at the end" (p. 231). Malmo interprets the research to indicate that increasing physiological activities are required to *sustain* performance and do not reflect *increased* motivation during performance. If this assertion is correct, we would expect to find that along with the organizing "plan" certain levels of activation of systems essential to performance are enforced.

One of the earlier investigations to bear this out, and also to substantiate the inverted U function of motivation in performance, was that of Stennett (1957). Stennett made a very sound case for substituting the notion of an "arousal continuum" for the discontinuous and artificial categories of emotion and motivation. In a carefully controlled experimental situation imposing graded levels of arousal upon his subjects, Stennett found, by recording muscle tension (EMG) gradients, an inverted U shaped relationship between arousal level and the accuracy of performance at a tracking task. He was able to confirm preceding findings (Surwillo, 1956; Bartoshuk, 1955; Smith, 1953) that the rising gradient of muscle tension is regular during task performance, but he added that its slope (steepness) is a function of level of motivation.

We then have dependable evidence that motivation to perform at a specific task sets up a "program" for essential physiological systems to follow. The level of activity of these systems, or the slope of the gradient which rises regularly from beginning to the end of task performance and then decreases rapidly, varies with the level of motivation to perform. When actual performance efficiency is correlated with level of arousal, it is found that performance is poorest under very high and very low conditions of motivation and most efficient at moderate levels. Now we would like to add a more cognitive factor and see how the subject's expectations for successful performance fit in with what we already know.

Diggory, Klein, and Cohen (1964) have produced a study to the point, relating muscle tension during performance to subjects' estimated probability of success at the task. Furthermore, they have summarized the work of other investigators and have concluded that research using muscle-action potentials have shown that muscle activity during performance of a task is increased by: (1) the duration of the task, (2) the increasing nearness of the goal or end of the task, (3) difficulty of the task, (4) distracting stimuli, (5) the value of the incentive offered, (6) the intelligence of the subject, and (7) previous failure rather than success. In relation to their own work, Diggory, *et al.* reported that in terms of measured muscle-action potentials, subjects who expected to succeed put forth more effort during performance than did those who expected to fail at the task. Interesting too is the demonstration by Smith (1953) that when subjects are not allowed to complete their task but were interrupted, muscle tension did not fall as after task completion, indicating the sustaining function of arousal or motivation. Horwitz, Glass, and Niyekawa (1964) have cited various experimental circumstances in which post-movement muscle tension was shown to vary with an approach-avoidance balance and the probability of success or failure. Their experiments showed that if the approach tendency exceeds the avoidance tendency, tension rises with increase in the probability of a successful outcome. Where the avoidance tendency is greatest, tension rises with the increase in probability of failure (p. 78).

MOTIVATION, DISABILITY, AND REHABILITATION

More to the point in relation to motivation and physical disability to performance, let us look at a few studies, first in relation to level of arousal or motivation in general and then in regard to the effects of success or failure and patients' estimates of the chances of success or failure.

Casella (1962) has reported a study involving sixty male right hemiplegic patients of recent onset who were tested with the Taylor Manifest Anxiety Scale and subsequently divided into High, Moderate, and Low anxiety groups. As measured by this means, patients' characteristic level of "anxiety" may be taken to mean their basal level of arousal. Physical therapy ratings initially and after six weeks of treatment in areas of ambulation, transfer, exercise, balance, coordination, and mood assessed relative functional improvement of the patients. The "Moderate anxiety" group made significantly greater improvement on all but balance and coordination, although the mean ratings for the three groups had been comparable initially. The "High anxious" group did better than the low, although neither had significant changes in mean ratings in any category.

Similarly, Ploski, Levita, and Riklan (1966) have shown a relationship between voluntary movement impairment and arousal level in parkinsonian patients. This was a study of forty-three hospitalized patients awaiting neurosurgery. In this instance, arousal level or activation level was determined by patient's basal electrodermal skin resistance. Significant correlations obtained indicated a negative relationship between activation level and voluntary movement impairment, increased impairment of motion being associated with decreased arousal. This requires some explanation since Subczynski, Matsumoto, Lin, and Cooper (1963) have previously demonstrated excessive arousal to interfere with voluntary movement in parkinsonian patients by increasing neuromuscular rigidity and tremor. The favored explanation for this apparent contradiction offered by Ploski, *et al.* is that increased arousal anticipating surgery in their patients produced increased physiological reactivity in general and probably did increase the severity of the symptoms of all their subjects. This effect was overshadowed, however, by the association of severe symptoms with decreased arousal, alertness, and responsivity. These results are particularly informative because they suggest that not only does arousal level affect performance, but also that restricted voluntary activity is a form of deprivation which reduces arousal level. This is probably only one of many complicated relations to be discovered between physical limitations, arousal or motivation, and performance abilities.

It should be apparent by now that effective treatment and rehabilitation will often call for either increasing or decreasing patient's level of arousal to achieve optimal results. An illustrative clinical study reported by Shatin, Brown, and Loizeaux (1961) has applied this principle. Two groups of subjects, male chronically ill patients, were matched on educational level and ratings of adjustment to hospitalization. Thirty-nine experimental group patients and fourteen controls were then included with ratings, interview data, and participation in activities used as the criteria for measuring "psychological remotivation." The experimental group was given a program which consisted of intensified recreational and rehabilitation activities by means of group therapy and more individual contact with staff. As expected, the experimental group showed significantly more gains, particularly in regard to morale and ward adjustment, as a result of the increased interest and effort of the staff toward them. This is one reported approach to increasing the arousal level or motivation level of chronically ill patients in a situation of prolonged deprivation, both environmental and physical. Such techniques were a fad in psychiatric treatment a few years ago, but little is heard about them now.

To proceed now to the effects of success and failure in motivation and performance, we must distinguish between the effects of success or failure at a task upon subsequent efforts and the effects of the patient's expectations for success or failure as determining his motivation for the task initially. Generally speaking, it has been found in normal subjects working at verbal or motor tasks that success and failure as outcomes both serve to decrease performance. Success because the goal has been attained, and failure because of the tendency to avoid repeating the situation again. This is, of course, an oversimplification, and the general finding has not held true in two studies of relevance (Benton, 1960; Garmezy & Harris, 1953) both dealing with brain damaged persons. Benton describes a series of investigations designed to test the effects of various instructional and feedback conditions on the performance of brain damaged persons. Conclusions reached were that such conditions as "urging and encouraging" decreased reaction time significantly, and instructions to "relax" decreased reactions times slightly. Success or failure instructions in the form of performance feedback had similar effects. Failure, however, had a substantially more significant result than success. For all of the results the gain for brain damaged subjects was greater than for controls because of the initially lower level of performance.

Garmezy and Harris had twenty-five cerebral palsied children as their subjects who were required to place pegs into a series of holes for four trials daily for fifteen days. Groups were provided verbal praise alone, verbal praise with candy rewards, or verbal reproof and loss of candy upon failure with speed of performance as the response measured. "The results clearly indicated that the invariant use of verbal praise, similar to the type usually employed by physical and occupational therapists during treatment, had little effect in modifying the motor behavior of cerebral palsied children. The introduction of material incentives, however, markedly improved their performance of a simple motor task" (p. 296). *Increments* in performance were again obtained under both success and failure conditions and appeared to be related to the presence rather than the achievement of the reward, since effects did not generalize to subsequent "neutral" trials when the incentive was absent. Both of these studies illustrate the Law-of-Initial-Value quite well in that the lower the level of performance initially, the greater the incremental effects of operations designed to raise performance.

Quite clearly, the effects of success and failure as outcomes in treatment and related retraining activities require much further study. This research is especially needed in view of the interpretation frequently made in various rehabilitation efforts that failures in training, in relearning activities of daily living, for example, have a detrimental effect upon subsequent performance due to the high level of emotional arousal which results. At least one study has indicated that the capacity to tolerate failure, which Atkinson and Feather describe as "persistence," is essential for rehabilitation. Davis (1955) rated

forty-eight paraplegic patients as to their "rehabilitation efficiency" and compared the upper and lower 25% on psychological test data and a frustrating situation of manual
performance. It was concluded that rehabilitation efficiency
was significantly related to tolerance for frustration, although
no relation could be confirmed for intelligence, personality, or
other psychological measures.

One cannot extrapolate freely the effects of success or failure
during rehabilitation from the results obtained from brain
damaged individuals (Benton; Garmezy & Harris). However,
we must think in terms of increasing task difficulty with increasing physiological limitations to the ability to perform
in many instances of treatment and rehabilitation. Within this
problem, an alternative solution presents itself in that "feedback" of results of a patient's efforts, whether in the form of
successful *or* unsuccessful attempts at a task, may in itself be
an important stimulus for motivation. The principles of feedback were described in detail in regard to perception previously
and will again become important in relation to the learning of
skills in a later section.

The expectation of success or failure, the patient's subjective
estimate of his chances of success, appears to be an entirely
different matter, and in this connection the patient will have
little or no objective basis for judging the adequacy of how he
will perform. We should expect to find, on the basis of some
results by Diggory, Klein, and Cohen and others, that patients who expect to succeed in rehabilitation programs will
put forth more effort and attain greater improvement in treatment than those who expect to fail. A personal investigation
conducted at the University of Colorado Medical Center was
designed to explore just this hypothesis of the relation of motivation to physical improvement (McDaniel, 1967).

This investigation was an attempt to apply certain theoretical
principles of decision-making processes, especially decision-
making under conditions of uncertainty, to the study of patients'

motivation for rehabilitation. One such principle is the "Subjective Probability Estimate" as expressed by decision theorists such as Edwards, Savage, Luce, and others. These, and other related concepts such as "utility," are mathematical concepts derived to explain how people make decisions in risky or uncertain situations and their preferences for certain outcomes. There is, presumably, a correlation between subjective probability and objective probabilities for all outcomes, although this is still being debated. Some recent studies in subjective probability have used a questionnaire approach (Brim & Hoff, 1957; Brim, 1955; Wallach & Kogan, 1959, 1961; and Feather, 1959) to study realistic individual situational variations. Fundamentally, the factors at work are: human beings consistently make choices based on the utilities of the outcomes and their subjective probabilities of success in attaining the outcomes; they tend to choose courses of action which will optimize gains and minimize losses based on their appraisal of the situation (Shelley & Bryan, 1964). It has even been shown that subjects who expect success put out more effort on a motor task than those who expect failure, as measured by muscle action potentials (Diggory, Klein & Cohen). The working hypotheses of this study were that the degree of physical improvement would be significantly and positively correlated with patients' subjective probabilities of successful outcomes, and that age and sex differences would be significant contributors.

The methodology employed in this study was adapted from the situational approach used by Wallach and Kogan, Feather, and Brim and consisted of a questionnaire constructed to obtain Ss estimates of outcome probabilities in regard to (1) occupational, physical, and financial independence, (2) activities of daily living, (3) functional physical improvement, and (4) changes in life style. The information was obtained by means of a structured personal interview in which patients were asked to make subjective probability estimates for ten separate items. Physicians' ratings of actual progress or improvement at discharge and severity of disability served as the index of treatment outcome and were correlated with patient response data.

Patients' subjective probability estimates were secured from forty individuals who were recently admitted patients of the Physical Medicine and Rehabilitation Department. Half of the group were men and half were women with subgroups counterbalanced for age above and below age forty-five. Subjects were instructed to give their estimates in terms of the chances out of one hundred, with 50-50 being even chances and above or below that indicating high or low chances.

The results of this investigation have shown that patients' improvement or progress is significantly related to their subjective estimates of the likelihood of outcomes associated with rehabilitation. Furthermore, age and sex differences in probability estimates were found even though neither factor was significantly related to patient progress. No relationship, on the other hand, between the severity of the patient's disability and either subjective probability estimates or progress at discharge was found. We apparently have isolated a comparatively pure "motivational" measure in relating the patient's estimates of his chances of attaining rehabilitation outcomes in terms of the areas measured, and the actual degree of improvement he is able to achieve in his physical medicine treatment program. This seems, therefore, to be a considerably more appropriate means of quantifying motivation than many clinical methods which have been tried.

As mentioned earlier, in order to make sense out of patient or client motivation in rehabilitation, it is necessary to conceptualize the whole process in terms of sequences of tasks to which the patient applies both his motivation and ability with varying degrees of success. Patient expectations for and responses to success or failure are only two of a number of specific divisions which could be made in the rehabilitation process to clarify the importance and mechanisms of motivation. Unfortunately, most of the promising avenues of research have not as yet been explored. One of the most fascinating problems for precise psychological studies that has only been touched upon is that of the patient's response to the complete or partial elimination or correction of his disability. Several such studies regarding responses to surgical intervention in epilepsy, cardiac disorders, hearing, and visual defects were mentioned in a previous chapter dealing with emotional responses to rehabilitation and treatment. We may add to these the patient's acceptance, training for, and use of artificial appliances and mechanical devices which serve to compensate for the disabling effects of the physical impairment. In regard to amputee acceptance and use of prostheses, for example, several studies (Campbell, Bansavage, Van Ormer & Dick, 1964; Weiss, 1959; Kransdorf, Fishman & Lifton, 1950) have implicated such factors as cosmetic appearance, sex, and age of the wearer as important variables to motivation for training and use of a prosthesis.

Likewise, there have been several studies of responses to cardiac surgery in particular which indicate that postsurgical adaptation depends very heavily upon "motivation." To illustrate the apparent effects of motivation in the results of cardiac surgery, two studies with very different results may be cited. The first, contributed by Bergy and Bruce (1955), was a study of thirty-one patients who were reevaluated at an average of twenty-one months following mitral valve surgery. It was found that the patients' attitudes toward heart disease and disability generally had improved greatly, whereas objective clinical improvement was only partial or moderate. In patients who considered themselves *subjectively* "better" following surgery (93%), there was a correlation with objective evidence in only about one half. Furthermore, the reported employment status of the group showed very definite improvement.

Contrast, now, the research of Priest, Zaks, Yacorzynski, and Boshes (1957) involving pre- and post-operative studies of sixty patients, primarily with rheumatic valvular deformities. Pre-operative testing showed the usual marked anxiety, but the anxiety level of the group worsened immediately post-operatively and did not improve on either six or twelve month follow-up measures.

There are perhaps many reasons why the results of two similar studies with the same etiological groups should differ, among the most likely being group differences in "motivation" for recovery and rehabilitation. Motivation could probably be related to pre- and post-operative medical management as well.

There are also indications in other respects, notably at present in chronic renal disease, that treatment procedures are capable of introducing changes in the motivational-emotional complexion of many patients. Hemodialysis of uremic patients by means of the artificial kidney has been shown by a number of contemporary investigations (Shea, Bogdan, Freeman & Schreiner, 1965; Wright, Sand & Livingston, 1966; Cooper, 1967) to be an especially psychologically and physically stressful experience, but for which there seems to be no alternative for many patients at present.

From another perspective in rehabilitation, the onset of disability, it appears that again the individual's motivations may be of vital importance. It must be borne in mind, however, that as interesting as the following results are, they can scarcely be considered as more than suggestive at the present time.

The notion of "psychological vulnerability" is a principle which is well known in psychiatry and psychosomatic medicine generally today, and in what has been called "Illness behavior" (Mechanic, 1962). Illness behavior is a sociological concept which itself has been the object of much recent attention and involves many variables which also may be thought of as being motivational in nature. The conception, however, has not been widely applied to traumatic or permanent physical disabilities, even though the principle of psychological vulnerability has many interesting research and clinical implications as shown by some precursory investigations.

Depressive affect, which has been linked to the frequency of illness and illness behavior (Kasl & Cobb, 1964), has also been found related to the occurrence of accidental injuries (Hirschfeld & Behan, 1966). Hirschfeld and Behan have reached the conclusion from extensive studies of industrial accident cases that a major factor at work is the victim's need to substitute an acceptable disability (physical) for an unacceptable one (psychological) since, "In our culture some disabilities receive such a degree of approval that the person is compensated for them" (p. 127). According to Hirschfeld and Behan, a characteristic of an "unacceptable" disability is depressive affect and, "In particular, we were able to confirm the existence of troubled life situations before the accidents occurred and to verify the essentially depressive nature of the patient's feelings during the prodrome" (p. 125). Their research has been based upon clinical studies of 500 injured workers for 50 of whom treatment consisted importantly of helping the disabled workers to find more effective solutions to their problems. Perhaps these findings may even be a partial explanation for the popular impression that industrially injured individuals make difficult rehabilitation clients, especially in vocational rehabilitation.

Regarding the interaction of affective and motivational factors, Loeb, Beck, Diggory, and Tuthill (1967) have reported an interesting investigation of subjective probability estimates in depressed patients. Their subjects were forty male outpatients who were classified by various criteria into high and low depressed groups. In an experimentally controlled situation, one-half of both high and low depressed groups either "succeeded" or "failed" at card sorting trials in which success and failure were predetermined and independent of actual performance. A visual display of his performance was provided each subject. Although the degree of depression had no effect upon actual performance, it was found that "The experiment clearly demonstrated that relatively highly depressed persons are more pessimistic than lightly depressed persons, e.g., they give lower probability-of-success estimates with regard to their chances of meeting a stated goal. Furthermore, the depressed groups evaluated their performance (which in reality was just as good) as poorer than did relatively non-depressed subjects" (p. 194). In general, it was also found that "success" facilitated the subsequent performance of highly depressed subjects, whereas "failure" was more motivating for low depressed subjects. The implications for rehabilitation are clear, especially since depression is a very common emotional response during illness and treatment. Depression can condition a patient's motivation for prescribed task performance, but "success" can be used to enhance performance.

Fordyce (1964) has studied the circumstances leading to the onset of spinal cord injuries in a group of fifty-eight male paraplegic and quadriplegic patients in a rehabilitation center. These were classified primarily as "imprudent behavior" contributing to the accident or as "chance or capricious onset." Those patients whose onset had been judged to be the result of their own imprudence were found in this study to be significantly younger and more impulsive. Fordyce recommends that further study be made into the significance of these factors in the rehabilitation process, particularly in regard to physical management. In instances of spinal cord injuries where secondary complications of bowel, bladder, and skin problems frequently arise, the role of "impulse-dominated" behavior in self-care may be significant. In a more recent study from the same laboratory, Kunce and Worley (1966) divided their patients as follows: "In the first analysis, we separated the cord injured Ss into two groups: one of Ss who were active agents in their accidents such as drivers of the automobile, participants in individual sports as skiing or tumbling; and the other of Ss who were passive agents in the accident, as being passengers, or victims of industrial equipment failure" (p. 106-07). The former class of patients expressed occupational interests more consistent with attitudes of adventurousness and physical activity than did the latter group of "passive agents." Furthermore, all spinal cord injured patients expressed such interests as a group significantly more than a comparison group of other disabled patients.

There were a number of investigations of relationships of psychological processes in behavior organization, regulation, and control which might have been included under the heading of motivation, but which were equally relevant to the understanding of emotional behavior and perceptual processes. The material has been included in other sections, and the reader would best consider the evidence thus presented in this and previous chapters as all contributing to the understanding of the central process of behavior regulation and control—not as isolated discussions which pertain only to emotion or to motivation or only to any other system of the regulating process.

CLINICAL IMPLICATIONS OF
MOTIVATIONAL CONCEPTS

As has been true of every other section of this volume, we must draw selectively upon empirical and theoretic principles to fill in the gaping lack of objective knowledge in regard to motivation and physical disability. Some highly relevant although largely untested ideas from a few behavioral scientists with implications for clinical rehabilitation technologies have thus been selected to attempt to apply existing information (Schlesinger, 1963 a,b; Zane, 1961; Zane & Lowenthal, 1960).

As Zane and Lowenthal have correctly pointed out, "good" and "poor" motivation are generally inferred from patient's cooperation and participation, and success or failures in rehabilitation programs. Clinically, they have divided cases showing "poor motivation" into three groups: " those who were reluctant or refused to try the prescribed task; those who tried and did poorly; those who did well at first and then regressed" (p. 400). These three classes of supposedly "poorly motivated" patients were illustrated with nine case histories. The one guiding conclusion reached by Zane and Lowenthal was that, "Motivation was poor or became poor in all of the cases presented when the patient performed worse or anticipated doing worse than he expected of himself. Motivation improved when therapeutic conditions were introduced which permitted the patient to achieve his goal" (p. 406). In other words, the authors' clinical impression is that the experience or anticipation of failure in the tasks prescribed in the patient's rehabilitation program account for behavior which may be described as "poorly motivated."

Actually, the conception of motivation for rehabilitation expressed by Zane and Lowenthal is more complete than this. In summary, they have stated:

> Motivation is seen as a complex of forces—some interfering with and some disposing towards effort and learning. Thus, negative and positive motivational factors exist. Negative motivational factors arise in states of increasing stress while positive motivational forces develop with decreasing stress. Clinically, increasing stress develops as the patient is unable or anticipates being unable to achieve what he is trying to do. Decreasing stress ensues as the patient becomes able or anticipates being able to achieve his goal (1960, p. 400).

We see now the conviction that motivation is in reality tied in with the patient or client's level of emotional arousal which, when too high, interferes with performance and in turn changes the directions that subsequent behavior may take. A more recent paper by Zane (1961) clarifies his position more fully.

The author has outlined what he believes to be the nature of the process of motivation to achieve some therapeutic objective and the most favorable therapeutic conditions for effective performance. Zane believes that it is far more productive to manipulate and change therapeutic conditions than to attempt to modify the patient's "motivation" or characteristic reactions to stress. He further assumes that any patient can learn under appropriate conditions, although at different rates and by various routes to the goal.

Analyzing patients' efforts as they fail, no matter for what reason, Zane finds that they are simultaneously mobilizing compensatory actions designed to deal with the task, the therapist, and their own subjective emotions. Poor performance, if allowed to stand by the therapist, sets up competing responses of avoidance and increased emotional arousal due to increased stress which can only result in further ineffective learning and performance. Zane interprets, "Effective learning, which requires highly discriminating operations, becomes impossible as the patient's attention becomes increasingly and irresistibly drawn away from the task to his state of rapid and uncontrollable disorganization of mental and physical capacities, dread and panic" (p. 233).

The secret of the problem of motivation to achieve a difficult objective through rehabilitation programs with such a conception as Zane (1961) provides is equally applicable to any technological approach and to any therapeutic objective. It follows that appropriate management creates conditions that allow the patient or client's attention to be maximally focused on a task or goal that is possible for him to achieve. Most rehabilitation counselors, for example, who by virtue of their task of coordinating many separate therapeutic efforts and objectives have a broader perspective than most other therapists concerned with the individual patient, have often been impressed by the ability of failure in one area or even extraneous factors to upset an entire rehabilitation plan.

It is essential that the patient's attention be focused on appropriate goals with the elimination of sources of interference and competing responses. Zane offers three guiding principles of effective management which are worthwhile recounting here. First, he states that the patient's attention can be more easily guided toward therapeutic goals when one begins with *effort* as the immediate goal, in which case any appropriate action approaches the goal. As has already been illustrated in preceding pages, motivation and effort are greatest the nearer the subject comes to attaining or approaching the performance goal. Zane asserts that success in this regard reduces stress, improves the patient's expectations for himself, and provides a greater sense of security in regard to the therapist. Second, Zane's motivational concept emphasizes that, "Selections are made of attainable and compatible goals, based upon experiences with the individual patient, which in sequence lead to achievement of the more distant prescribed goal" (p. 237). In general, it is correctly recommended that difficult or frustrating therapeutic objectives be divided into more immediately attainable components which are of more recognizable significance to the patient. The third recommendation involves the use of "feedback" to the patient of the results of his efforts, which means the discrete use of criticism and praise so that mistakes can be corrected. The use of feedback principles is important in learning and in maintaining effective performance levels as will be further discussed in the section to follow on the conditions for skilled performance. Clearly, throughout Zane's clinical approach there is paramount importance placed upon the therapeutic relationship itself which of course is controllable by the therapist. Some additional viewpoints of this problem will be of value.

Schlesinger (1963a,b) suggests that many "motivational" problems are not due to patient characteristics entirely, but are equally brought about by the nature of the institutions and agencies and the relationships and settings involved in rehabilitation. Schlesinger's group and environmental clinical research have some important implications for rehabilitation practices which should be emphasized. The most significant cause, as well as remedy, for patient behavior problems have been indicated by Schlesinger (1963 b) to be the patient-therapist relationship and the general interpersonal structure of the institution or agency. This writer stresses that, "The effective staff member learns to perceive his own behavior as a deliberate instrument for modifying patient behavior" (1963b, p. 365). This also applies equally well to all rehabilitation personnel whether physician, counselor, or therapist, since all are concerned with the often difficult and demanding task of changing patient behavior.

Schlesinger (1963a) has indicated the major characteristics of institutions and agencies serving the physically disabled which in themselves create behavioral obstacles to successful rehabilitation. Sociologically, it has been suggested that the rehabilitation center, for example, provides complete care and assumes total responsibility for all aspects of the patient's life. It is little wonder that entry and termination at such an institution are most stressful experiences for a great many clients (Krause, 1964), as mentioned previously. In the hierarchy of authority, the patient is on the bottom and finds himself in a most powerless position. Schlesinger interprets that, "The hospital provides little opportunity for mature, autonomous, self-directed responsible behavior. Certainly this complete control over the behavior of the patient is warranted in the phase of recovery from the acute accident, but the question may be raised of its justifiability for longer periods of time" (p. 248).

Schlesinger has indicated, too, that patients adopt a variety of methods of dealing with these circumstances.

> With little opportunity for direct control, the patients may respond to the control apparatus in several different ways: (1) The patient may respond with complete apathy and lack of involvement. (2) The patient may be rebellious and refuse to cooperate with the staff. (3) The patient may be a 'colonizer,' taking up 'permanent' residence in

the hospital, a more benign atmosphere for him than the harsher world outside. He will accept the authority system as part of the environment he has to put up with. (4) Patients may become 'converts,' actively promulgating the party line. These patients take over the official staff picture of themselves and try to act out the role of the perfect inmate. They may even take over the attitudes of the staff toward other patients and urge them to conform to the house rules. This phenomenon has been noted among concentration camp inmates by Bettelheim. Many of the older inmates identified with their captors, wore bits of the guards discarded clothing, and behaved toward the other concentration camp members even more brutally than did the guards. (5) And, finally, the patient may elect to 'play it cool.' This kind of feigned interest in the program allows the person to participate without undergoing any real change (p. 248).

Schlesinger (1963a) advocates a gradual increase during treatment in the responsibility and decision-making participation of clients in the rehabilitation program whose primary "obligation" is to learn improved physical, personal, and social skills. If we accept the principle that all rehabilitation fields should be concerned with restoring the maximum degree of self-control to their patients or clients, Schlesinger's recommendation is essential for a desirable outcome and for optimal motivation for therapeutic goals as well.

More concerned in a later paper with staff-patient interactions, Schlesinger (1963b) has separated two major staff functions. "One is to help the patient learn new behaviors covering the wide range of sensory, motor, perceptual, emotional, cognitive, and social aspects. The second is to motivate the patient, reducing the psychological costs of learning for the patient and increasing his rewarding social-emotional experiences" (p. 362). He points out, too, that not only is patient depersonalization and standardization at odds with the requirements of "good motivation," but that often staff-patient differences in expectations and goals are a frequent source of unnecessary obstacles. That clients have their own expectations and goals, subjective probability estimates, and make many subjective decisions regardless of the behavior of the staff, is a definite fact that may at times frustrate those who prescribe for them. The effects of depersonalization, standardization, and authoritative constraints, which exist mainly for staff protection, can only serve to establish the gulf between client and therapist which may be widened by the staff's lack of awareness of the motivational or behavioral effects of such obstacles.

Schlesinger (1963b) has suggested that the primary tasks of all therapeutic workers is to attempt to induce *changes* in the "content, direction or frequency" of patients' behavior. Change, of course, is resisted by all, patient and staff; but for the patient, the changes he is induced to make take on a somewhat different meaning. "Changes in behavior may be seen by the patient as involving high costs. Many of the changes require the expenditure of energy, personal discomfort, and physical pain" (p. 364). Another source of resistance is due to uncertainty, a provocation for anxiety and emotional distress which becomes associated first with injury or disease, with hospitalization and treatment, and later with the necessity of making many modifications in style of life. Neither change nor uncertainty is tolerated well in human behavior control processes, but this does not require a physical disability to potentiate. Schlesinger concludes, "The staff member needs to learn to view patient frustration-instigated behavior as a form of feedback. Instead of defensively evaluating patient behavior as a threat, these resistances to change may be viewed as information telling the therapist what is preventing him from being on target in accomplishing patient change" (p. 365).

We would have to summarize much of the research presented in this section with regard to motivation for rehabilitation in the same way as have Barry and Malinovsky (1965) in their timely review. "A major impression from the reports and research reviewed is that the concept of motivation is almost too broad, too complex, and too inclusive to usefully stimulate and aid in the improvement of rehabilitation practice and research" (p. 51).

Hopefully, however, a somewhat novel and more systematically meaningful conception of the organization of behavior in relation to physical disability and rehabilitation has been presented in this section than has previously been set forth. The reader is once again cautioned against the conception of "motivation" as a unitary phenomenon of human behavior which exists and can be dealt with distinctly from other aspects of behavioral regulation and control. The discussions in previous sections concerning emotional behavior, perceptual processes, and the one to follow relative to learning, are all equally relevant to the problems of behavior organization and changes in organization with physical illness and disability.

References

Atkinson, J. & Feather, N. *A Theory of Achievement Motivation.* 1966, Wiley, New York.

Barry, J. & Malinovsky, M. Client motivation for rehabilitation: A review. 1965, *Univ. Fla. Rehab. Res. Monogr. No. 1.*

Bartoshuk, A. Electromyographic gradients as indicants of motivation. *Canad. J. Psychol.*, 1955, **9**, 215-30.

Benton, A. Motivational influences on performance in brain damaged patients. *Amer. J. Orthopsychiat.*, 1960, **30**, 315-21.

Bergy, G. & Bruce, R. Discrepancies between subjective and objective responses to mitral commissurotomy. *New Eng. J. Med.*, 1955, **253**, 887-91.

Brim, O. Attitude content-intensity and probability expectations. *Amer. Sociol. Rev.*, 1955, **20**, 68-76.

Brim, O. & Hoff, D. Individual and situational differences in desire for certainty. *J. Abnor. Soc. Psychol.*, 1957, **54**, 225-9.

Campbell, E., Bansavage, J., Van Ormer, J. & Dick, E. The psychological and social factors related to successful prosthetic training in juvenile amputees. *ICIB*, 1964, **3**, 1-9.

Casella, C. A behavioral test of activation theory for hemiplegic patients. *Arch. PM&R*, 1962, **43**, 321-3.

Cooper, A. Hypomanic psychosis precipitated by hemodialysis. *Comprehen. Psychiat.*, 1967, **8**, 168-74.

Davis, D. An investigation of the relationship of frustration tolerance of paraplegics and the degree and rate of success in rehabilitation. *Diss. Abstr.*, 1955, **15**, 1262.

Diggory, J. & Morlock, H. Level of aspiration, or probability of success? *J. Abnor. Soc. Psychol.*, 1964, **69**, 282-9.

Diggory, J., Klein, S. & Cohen, M. Muscle action potentials and estimated probability of success. *J. Exper. Psychol.*, 1964, **68**, 449-55.

Feather, N. Success probability and choice behavior. *J. Exper. Psychol.*, 1959, **58**, 257-66.

Fordyce, W. Personality characteristics in men with spinal cord injury as related to manner of onset of disability. *Arch. PM&R*, 1964, **45**, 321-5.

Garmezy, N. & Harris, J. Motor performance of cerebral palsied children as a function of their success or failure in achieving material reward. *Child Dev.*, 1953, **24**, 287-300.

Hirschfeld, A. & Behan, R. The accident process III. Disability: Acceptable and unacceptable. *JAMA*, 1966, **197**, 125-9.

Horwitz, M., Glass, D. & Niyekawa, A. Muscular tension: Physiological activation or psychological act. In *Psychobiological Approaches to Social Behavior*. (Liederman & Shapiro, Eds.) 1964, Stanford University Press, Palo Alto.

Kasl, S. & Cobb, S. Some psychological factors associated with illness behavior and selected illnesses. *J. Chron. Dis.*, 1964, **17**, 325-45.

Kransdorf, M., Fishman, S. & Lifton, W. Study of amputee acceptance of prosthetic devices. *J. Phys. Ment. Rehab.*, 1950, **4**, 17-19.

Krause, E. On the Time and Place of Crises. New Eng. Rehab. Cent., Boston, 1964 (mimeo).

Kunce, J. & Worley, B. Interest patterns, accidents and disability. *J. Clin. Psychol.*, 1966, **22**, 105-07.

Lashley, K. The problem of serial order in behavior. In *Cerebral Mechanisms in Behavior*. Hixon Sympos. (Jeffres, Ed.) 1948.

Locke, E. Interaction of ability and motivation in performance. *Percept. Mot. Skills*, 1965, **21**, 719-25.

Loeb, A., Beck, A., Diggory, J. & Tuthill, R. Expectancy, level of aspiration, performance, and self-evaluation in depression. *Proceed. 75th Ann. Convent., APA*, 1967, 193-4.

Malmo, R. Physiological gradients and behavior. *Psychol. Rev.*, 1965, **64**, 225-33.

McDaniel, J. Relation of Subjective Probability Estimates to Patient Progress. In VRA proj. RT-10, progress report No. 3, Univ. Colo. School Med., Denver, 1967 (mimeo).

Mechanic, D. The concept of illness behavior. *J. Chron. Dis.*, 1962, **15**, 184-94.

Miller, G., Galanter, E. & Pribram, K. *Plans and the Structure of Behavior*. 1960, Holt, New York.

Parsons, T. Definitions of health and illness in the light of American values and social structure. In *Patients, Physicians and Illness*. (Jaco, Ed.) 1958.

Ploski, H., Levita, E. & Riklan, M. Impairment of voluntary movement in Parkinson's Disease in relation to activation level, autonomic malfunction, and personality rigidity. *Psychosom. Med.*, 1966, **28**, 70-7.

Priest, W., Zaks, M., Yacorzynski, G. & Boshes, B. The neurologic, psychiatric and psychologic aspects of cardiac surgery. *Med. Clins. No. Amer.*, 1957, **41**, 155-69.

Schlesinger, L. Staff authority and patient participation in rehabilitation. *Rehab. Lit.*, 1963 a, **24**, 247-9.

Schlesinger, L. Staff tensions and needed skills in staff-patient interactions. *Rehab. Lit.*, 1963 b, **24**, 362-5.

Scodel, H., Ratoosh, P. & Minas, J. Some personality correlates of decision making under conditions of risk. *Behav. Sci.*, 1959, **4**, 19-28.

Shatin, L., Brown, P. & Loizeaux, M. Psychological remotivation of the chronically ill medical patient. A quantitative study in rehabilitation methodology. *J. Chron. Dis.*, 1961, **14**, 452-68.

Shea, E., Bogdan, D., Freeman, R. & Schreiner, G.   Hemodialysis for chronic renal failure. IV Psychological considerations. *Ann. Inter. Med.,* 1965, **62,** 558-63.

Shelley, M. & Bryant, G.   *Human Judgements and Optimality,* 1964, Wiley, New York.

Smith, A.   An electromyographic study of tension in interrupted and completed tasks. *J. Exper. Psychol.,* 1953, **46,** 32-6.

Stennett, R.   The relationship of performance level to level of arousal. *J. Exper. Psychol.,* 1957, **54,** 54-61.

Subczynski, J., Matsumota, K., Lin, T. & Cooper, I.   The influence of various stimuli upon parkinsonian tremor and rigidity. *J. Neurol. Neurosurg. Psychiat.,* 1963, **26,** 269-76.

Surwillo, W.   Psychological factors in muscle action potentials: EMG gradients. *J. Exper. Psychol.,* 1956, **53,** 263-72.

Vroom, V.   *Work and Motivation.* 1964, Wiley, New York.

Wallach, M. & Kogan, N.   Aspects of judgement and decision-making: Interrelationships and change with age. *Behav. Sci.,* 1961, **6,** 23-36.

Wallach, M. & Kogan, N.   Sex differences and judgement processes. *J. Personality,* 1959, **27,** 555-64.

Weiss, S.   The relationship between personality traits and acceptance of prosthetic devices. *J. Phys. Ment. Rehab.,* 1950, **4,** 17-19.

Wright, R., Sand, P. & Livingston, G.   Psychological stress during hemodialysis for chronic renal failure. *Ann. Inter. Med.,* 1966, **64,** 611-21.

Zane, M. & Lowenthal, M.   Motivation in rehabilitation of the physically handicapped. *Arch. PM&R,* 1960, **41,** 400-07.

Zane, M. A view of the psychiatric principles in the management of rehabilitation problems. In *The Geriatric Amputee.* 1961, Nat. Acad. Sci., Publication 919.

Chapter VI

REGULATION AND CONTROL OF BEHAVIOR: LEARNING AND SKILLED PERFORMANCE

THE STUDY of the processes of learning and perception was the initial concern of scientific psychology and the pre-occupation of the earliest laboratories. In fact, there are those today who, with considerable justification, urge that psychology should restrain itself to the study of those phenomena and forget about extraneous subjects such as psychopathology. At any rate, both perception and learning have been extensively investigated historically from the standpoint of the conditions under which they operate rather than the mechanisms of the processes themselves. It has only been relatively recently, due to technological advances in neurophysiology, that much attention has been paid to substrates and physiological activities which make learning and perception possible. In the study of learning, especially, one is able to identify a great many different theories of the conditions under which it takes place, along with experimental evidence to support the contention. Even most general psychology texts today carry adequate discussions of the major principles of learning such as reinforcement, generalization, discrimination and so on, which will not be discussed in detail in this section. Instead we will focus on a relatively few clinically important and essential components of the learning of specific skills, notably attention and feedback, with the addition of the handful of studies relative to human physical limitations.

No great interest has been shown in investigating the effects of physical disabilities upon learning with the exceptions of sensory defects such as deafness and blindness and cerebral lesions. Each of these conditions imposes obviously severe limitations upon learning and performance primarily because they limit the individual's capacity to receive and process information perceptually. Structural limitations such as paralysis, amputation, and other kinds of more subtle physiological variations have not been thoughtfully investigated. Perhaps it has been the obviousness of physical barriers to performance that has led most investigators to ignore research with these problems, but in rehabilitation it is the problems of abilities and disabilities that are our paramount concerns.

Conceptual definitions of both *learning* and *skill* must be provided in the interest of bringing problems more sharply into focus. Learning, as an indispensable subsystem in the process of behavior regulation and control, has been defined as the acquisition and modification of the means of behavior regulation and control. Hence, all learning is considered to be "instrumental" by definition. It is only possible by virtue of perception, motivation, and emotional arousal and is therefore quite dependent upon other subsystems in the central regulating process. Skill, on the other hand, is a matter of the quality of control. It implies intrinsic, self-regulating and self-controlling mastery, i.e., finely coordinated control of the essential systems for performance, sensory and motor. Conceptually, it does not matter whether the skill in question is athletic performance, machine operation, walking, or speaking.

In a way, the inclusion of this section is redundant since all of the important components such as perception, emotion, and motivation have already been discussed along with some effects of physical disability. However, there are a few additional points which have not been mentioned before and should now receive our attention. Just to mention some of the variables discussed under other headings, there is probably not one on the following list which could not be demonstrated to affect learning and performance in addition to actual physical impairment and limitation.

TABLE 6

FACTORS INFLUENCING LEARNING AND PERFORMANCE

Emotional Factors +	Perceptual Factors +	Motivational Factors
anxiety and distress	self-perception,	decision-making
level of arousal	cognition	achievement motive
somatic	body-image	level of motivation
preoccupation	self-concept	ability and motivation
sensory isolation	internal sensations	success/failure
social isolation	somatic	success probability
restricted mobility	preoccupations	treatment procedures
situational stress	phantom perceptions	therapeutic management
subjective pain	altered or absent	psychological
severity of disability	sensation	vulnerability
depression and	sensory compensation	patient-staff
denial	lateral differences	interaction
	in input	
	spatial/temporal	
	feedback	

The list, of course, is not exhaustive, but clinical and empirical illustrations could be given for each one to suggest an influence upon learning and performance in rehabilitation. For some, much is already known, particularly for sensory isolation, level of arousal, or level of motivation. The rest remain unexplored territory for some creative investigator.

K.U. Smith's cybernetic or neurogeometric theory which was reviewed in the section on perception is equally useful in considering learning and skilled performance (Smith & Henry, 1966; Smith, 1966). Smith and Henry have pointed out that the traditional views of learning assume that the emission of discrete responses is learned independently and strengthened by repetition and reinforcement, which does not explain the infinite variation in response patterning and organization possible in human beings. "Cybernetic theory interprets response specialization in terms of the spatial characteristics of feedback-control patterns, suggesting that the basis of learned variability in behavior lies in the limitless possibilities for spatial variations in motor sensory interactions. Thus we believe that the specialized response that is learned, remembered, and transferred is defined by the directional characteristics of both the movement and the controlling sensory inputs" (p. 37).

Through learning and development the individual establishes a repertoire of specific patterns of motor sensory control. The extent to which these patterns can be modified and adapted to other activities relies upon an accumulated memory record from which can be selected those patterns of control most likely to be appropriate. The selection and refinement of control only results from practice, modification, and generalization. Diseases, injuries, or other limitations can influence learning, transfer, and memory because of their interference and limitation of controlling and regulating mechanisms. Smith has shown in many experiments that learning and performance may be easily disrupted by temporal and spatial displacements of feedback, and also that feed-forward, or anticipation, is not possible when feedback is disturbed. The cybernetic conception of learning, which depends most heavily upon feedback as a substitute for reinforcement and perceptual processes in general, is very well summed up as follows:

> The cybernetic view of learning is that it involves improvements in continuous control patterns rather than associations established between temporally contiguous discrete events. This view in effect substitutes spatial determinism for temporal determinism in learning change, for improved response comes about through the individual's

ability to detect spatial differences in sensory feedback patterns and to regulate his movements accordingly (Smith & Henry, 1966, p. 35).

However, another form of feedback which very definitely deserves mention is in the form of information feedback or "knowledge of results" of performance: Knowledge of results (KR) or information feedback (IF) in this context usually refers to extrinsic, supplementary feedback promoting the conscious awareness of, and attention to the effects of the subject's own actions. Bilodeau (1966) asserts the following empirical and theoretical properties of KR: "Probably most psychologists would allow that IF has at least the following three empirical properties regardless of hypothesized theoretical properties: (a) R strengthening, (b) sustaining performance, and (c) eliminating previously established Rs. As for its theoretical properties IF, as any stimulus, can have all or any of three: (a) directive, (b) motivating, and (c) reinforcing" (p. 257). In other words, KR or IF is a means of augmenting the stimulus consequences of behavior.

Operationally, KR can be provided effectively by verbal reports from other persons, visual or any other sensory display of actual performance of a task. Temporal factors are significant, i.e., the greater the lag between behavior and KR, the less information the feedback apparently conveys. Bilodeau points out, however, that delays and displacements are not the only important factors. The time between KR and the next response and the time interval between successive Rs is also apparently significant. It is generally considered that a relatively short time interval (5-10 secs.) between KR and the next response is preferable, whereas a moderate interval between successive responses seems acceptable. In terms of frequency, it seems that extrinsic KR does not have to follow every response, although intrinsic feedback certainly follows every action.

Conceivably, in many types of physical disabilities where intrinsic IF suffers from delayed transmission, spatial displacement, or is partially or totally absent, extrinsic KR may be substituted effectively. Supplementary feedback would, therefore, be of value in many kinds of training situations found in rehabilitation and treatment.

A few studies will now be mentioned which have applied extrinsic KR in some form to therapy and training. Madison and Herring (1960) developed, for patients with impaired hand function, a means to produce a graphic, easily read record of progress and performance. It involved an electromechanical apparatus to record finger movements including the range and speed of movement. For this study, 34 patients were divided into matched groups of 17 each; but of the original group, only 11 in the experimental and 5 in the control group finished the experiment due to treatment dropouts. The procedure was to pretest both groups using a variety of standardized perceptual-motor tests and the finger movement device. During the next two weeks experimental patients were tested once each week using the finger movement technique, whereas the controls were not. Following this, all subjects were retested with the standardized measures. The results were encouraging and in the predicted direction, although not statistically significant probably due to insufficient numbers of subjects, insufficient trials, and insensitive criteria for motor improvement. The authors felt that a larger, more controlled study would confirm that this type of supplemental feedback would lead to faster improvement in hand performance.

Andrews (1964) has described a procedure whereby neuromuscular reeducation of hemiplegic patients could be facilitated through visual and audible displays of muscle action potentials. The report is of application of the procedure to twenty patients in an attempt to assist the patient to generate voluntary motor activity in a non-functional muscle. The method would supplant interrupted proprioception in hemiplegia. Andrews' procedure was first to illustrate the desired response by recording from a normal muscle. When the patient understood the sound and appearance on an oscilloscope of the voluntary muscle action potential, the procedure was switched to a paretic muscle. Passive movement of the joint moved by the muscle was necessary which the patient was instructed to follow through, his attention always being directed to the extrinsic feedback sources. The results were that seventeen out of the twenty patients tested were able to generate "motor unit action potentials capable of producing strong, voluntary, controlled action of that muscle" within a five-minute trial period.

Procedures for conditioning conscious motor unit control through auditory and visual monitoring have recently been refined by Simard and Basmajian (1967) and Basmajian, Baeza, and Fabrigar (1965) with normal subjects. Simard and Basmajian describe the procedure as follows: "Subjects are provided with auditory and visual cues of the motor unit activity through electromyography combined with innate proprioceptive impulses. Certain conditions are shown to be necessary for optimal results: a calm atmosphere, clear-cut commands, mandatory rest periods, a step-wise training schedule, and finally, highly competent direction of the training procedure" (p. 12).

Trombly (1966) has proposed using feedback principles as a more efficient means of training than conventional methods. The author very clearly points out some unfortunate circumstances in training physically disabled persons to use mechanical devices. "Conventionally, therapists indiscriminately surround patients with encouragement and attention. The less the patient tries to become independent the more attention he receives from the therapist who is trying to encourage him and convince him of the advantages of being independent. The patient soon discovers, however, that when he begins to try to become independent the therapist tends to withdraw and to leave him on his own" (p. 217).

Trombly has suggested using feedback principles in training quadriplegic persons to use various models of powered hand splints, the recommended procedures designed to reinforce the instrumental responses of grasping and controlling objects. The approach utilizes verbal feedback of performance results by the therapist, the patient's own sources of proprioceptive feedback in the movements used to guide the device, and, of course, visual recognition of appropriately guided actions. In addition, a standard set of tasks is employed by which the patient can be concretely shown improved or poor performance with subsequent trials.

Several important principles are illustrated in these preliminary studies which must be emphasized. First is the use of supplementary feedback channels to substitute for the normal information input. Second, the feedback must be in a form of information that is readily recognized and processed by the patient. It is immediate and unequivocal, even if pretraining is necessary. Third, the feedback must be a direct result of the action and does not occur for any other response. Note, however, that positive and negative feedback are required to correct errors, i.e., the patient must know exactly how and when he has done the wrong thing as well as the right thing in order to make a discriminative response. Finally, instructions should be precise; there must be minimal distraction and interference, and no competing responses. Rest intervals separating trials are also recommended.

There is, on the other hand, some experimental evidence that learning is possible in the absence of normal information feedback. Taub, Bacon, and Berman (1965) report a study in which seven male rhesus monkeys were subjected to right forelimb, neck, and shoulder deafferentation by intradural section of the dorsal roots from C2 to T3. Two weeks postoperatively, avoidance conditioning was begun in which the conditioned stimulus was a single click 3 1/2 seconds prior to a shock to the left forearm. Flexion of the right (deafferent) forelimb after the click and before the shock avoided the shock. It was observed that the subjects made no use of the deafferented extremity in a free situation; however, all Ss learned the flexion conditioned response. Deafferented subjects required significantly longer to learn the response than intact animals. It is important that a screen prevented the subjects from obtaining visual feedback information of their responses as well. In a subsequent investigation, Taub, Ellman, and Berman subjected three monkeys to deafferentation of *both* forelimbs by bilateral intradural section of dorsal roots C2 to T3. All three were able to learn a conditioned grasp response to avoid shock in the absence of somatic afferent and visual information feedback. It was found to be important during conditioning that the arm be left free rather than im- mobilized. Deafferent Ss were able to transfer the conditioned response to the contralateral limb successfully, whereas intact animals did not and continued to make inappropriate responses with the original limb. The grasp response in deafferent sub- jects was found as powerful as the grasp in the intact subjects.

Taub, Ellman, and Berman (1966) have concluded, as a result of their work and contrary to conventional neurological views, that "Work in our laboratory during the past eight years has demonstrated that somatic sensation is not necessary for the performance of voluntary movement . . . . Forearm flexion, however, is admittedly a crude movement. It remained possible that tactile and proprioceptive feedback are necessary for the performance of finer, more complex movement of the distal musculature" (p. 593). Their conditioned grasp response study, however, eliminated the latter possibility. The authors interpreted the finding that deafferented subjects transferred the conditioned grasp response immediately to the other hand while intact subjects did not, indicating that the movements of one limb exert an inhibitory influence upon the other and deafferentation abolishes this influence. Taub, *et al.,* have concluded, "In general, these results tend to confirm and extend our previous findings concerning the range of con- ditioned movement that is possible in a deafferented limb. It is clear that even movements of the distal musculature can be learned and performed in the absence of somatic afferent feedback" (p. 594).

These results are disquieting to say the least, not only from the point of view of traditional neurology but traditional and contemporary learning theory as well. The finding that neither proprioceptive nor visual feedback of information is essential for learning and coordinating even relatively complex voluntary movements must at the very least force us to reexamine and investigate more thoroughly the hypothesized and previously demonstrated role of feedback of information in learning and performance. Furthermore, the results have far - reaching implications for the retraining of physically disabled persons whose problems involve important deafferentation of the extremities.

Problems wherein proprioception is disrupted unilaterally, such as in hemiplegia, are complicated by cortical lesions as typically encountered in cerebral palsy and cerebrovascular lesions. Extensive perceptual studies (Birch, Belmont & Karp, 1967, 1965, 1964) have indicated that in hemiplegia the whole process of excitation-inhibition affecting both incoming information and outgoing responses is the major interference to relearning. The interference seems to result from a lag in information processing in the damaged hemipshere and increased time required for recovery from prior stimulation. Loss of peripheral sensory input is but of relatively minor importance to relearning with hemiplegia. Nevertheless, there is suggestive research which indicates that voluntary responses can be conditioned in the paretic limb among hemiplegic patients, notably simple motor responses (Van Buskirk, 1954; Hellebrandt, 1951; Cernacek, 1961), forearm flexion to escape electric shock (Ince, Sokolow & Menon, 1966), and other instrumental responses (Goodkin, 1966). These results, however, must be regarded as inconclusive at the present time, and although not wishing to dwell on the complex problems of learning and deficits occurring with cortical lesions, some very interesting and encouraging clinical reports of both dominant and non-dominant hemispherectomy have recently appeared which are worthwhile mentioning. An excellent guide for the student wishing to pursue the problems of neuropsychology further is to be found in Louttit (1966).

Clinical reports have been furnished by Smith and Burklund (1966, 1967) of the progress of two middle-aged male survivors of surgical removal of one complete hemisphere of the cerebral cortex. The earlier report concerns a forty-seven year old male patient, right-handed and right-eyed, who continued to show improved function in a number of areas of behavior following complete removal of the left cerebral hemisphere (dominant). The account proceeds as follows: Immediately following surgery the patient showed right hemiplegia, right hemianopsia, and severe aphasia, although retaining the ability to follow verbal instruction. During the seven month post-operative period covered by this report, the patient at first began to repeat words, phrases, and sentences on command and was trained to write left-handed. Five months post-operatively he was able to answer simple questions, recall whole familiar songs, and correctly associated printed word and object. Writing, however, showed little further improvement. Within six months the patient showed greatly increased attention span and verbal comprehension, although with marked variability in susceptibility to fatigue and distraction. Emotional behavior remained appropriate with no noticeable change from premorbid reactivity, according to his family. No improvement in the right hemiplegia or hemianopsia occurred during the period.

The second case reported by Smith and Burklund (1967) is of removal of the right cerebral hemisphere (non-dominant) in a forty-four year old right-handed male patient. Left hemianopsia followed surgery but left motor function improved sufficiently to allow independent ambulation within one month. Speech, hearing, reading, writing, and general intelligence were all regarded as normal one week after surgery. Emotional behavior was appropriate. This patient has been restudied at two, five, seven, ten, and fifteen years post-operatively with the major persistent deficits found in retention, memory, and spatial orientation. The patient has remained unable to shift rapidly his point of visual focus or to maintain spatial orientation. He has been unable to distinguish left from right in space or body orientation.

Smith and Burklund (1966, 1967) have concluded in comparing the results of both dominant and non-dominant hemispherectomy in these two right-handed male patients that differences in the functions of the cerebral hemispheres (and hence the relearning possible) are mainly quantitative rather than qualitative and strictly localized. There are many who could agree with their conclusion, and it seems that the historical division of verbal and motor functions to the left and right cerebral hemispheres respectively and the retraining efforts of rehabilitation may be in need of revision.

In all rehabilitation efforts, the problems of learning and relearning are of imminent concern, often from many differing points of view of a particular patient and his needs. A group of contemporary workers in the area of learning (Meyerson, Michael, Mowrer, Osgood & Staats, 1963) has conceptualized the relationships of learning in rehabilitation as, "Habilitation (original learning), dishabilitation (modifications of behavior resulting from the condition of disability), and rehabilitation (the new learning, unlearning, and relearning which lead to adjustment)" (p. 109). We are not, however, typically interested only in accomplishing training and retraining, but also in assisting patients to achieve and maintain optimally skilled performance. Therefore, we must consider the problem not only in terms of immediate acquisition of the means of behavior regulation and control but in terms of continuing effort and application of these means over a prolonged period of time, perhaps the lifetime of the individual. Let us consider briefly, therefore, requirements in addition to the capacity to learn and other elements of the process of acquisition.

There has been much recent research which would demonstrate that inherent human limitations in attention and retention are most fundamental to the establishment and maintenance of skilled performance (Posner, 1966). In other words, we should also pay strict attention to the processing, storage, and recall of information and response patterns. This is an exceedingly complex matter from the research point of view but can be explained relatively easier in general principle.

First we must expect to deal with the limitations of attention, which is the human organism's primary means of selecting and processing relevant information. The demands are that the patient-subject be able to perceive, select, and facilitate transmission of relevant information while inhibiting irrelevant, extraneous, or distracting stimuli. When man performs a simple task he is simultaneously able to attend to other events as well, but as Posner has pointed out, "As the difficulty of a task increases, it demands more of man's limited attention, and the spare capacity available for dealing with other signals is reduced" (p. 1714). This investigator indicates that this state of affairs changes with practice, but even at that, the initially difficult task will continue to require more attention even after considerable practice. It should be quite clear that since physical limitations often make even the ordinary everyday tasks difficult in rehabilitation, attention becomes a most important variable in performance.

Posner's evidence also includes that skilled performance requires the integration of present input with retained previous experience. Posner has confirmed the importance of both information processing capacity and storage capacity as crucial in determining performance levels. He states, "The important point here is that the degree of distraction, or of attention given the intervening task, can be manipulated, and that this degree of distraction is systematically related to the amount of forgetting" (p. 1715). It has also been illustrated that retained information loses its precision and decays over time, the rate of decay or "forgetting" being a function of the number and similarity of items of information to be stored. In regard to language skills, for example, Posner suggests, "Since many language skills demand the continuous intake, storage, and recall of information, such skills provide nearly optimum conditions for the occurrence of forgetting. The intake of new items tends to block rehearsal, while the competition from earlier items leads to a rapid loss in precision. Because of the rapid loss of stored information in such situations, memory limitations are basic to the information processing analysis of many skills" (pp. 1716-17). There are many types of skills which require the retention of sensory information and visual or proprioceptive patterns, i.e., the spatial control patterns of movements which are not coded in verbal symbols. Posner would agree with Smith's assertions in that he has inferred, "Nonverbal information concerning the distance, form, and location of prior movements must be stored between successive trials" (p. 1717).

It should be recognized that in most aspects of rehabilitation we will be dealing not only with inherent limitations of information processing and retention but also with limitations superimposed by physical damage and dysfunction which may affect information processing and storage channels, the mechanisms for responding, or both. Many perceptual and emotional distractions and interferences also will intervene, and the tasks that are typically required of the patient are thus made increasingly difficult. For these reasons, it has repeatedly been emphasized that the perceptual, emotional, and motivational factors are all intertwined and interact with the difficulty of the task which is prescribed for the patient. Clearly, labeling slow progress and improvement or even regression of a patient as due to "poor motivation," "uncooperativeness," or the like is a naive statement indeed.

We should suspect that more than we presently dream could reasonably be expected to be accomplished in therapeutic management, vocational rehabilitation, and generally all phases of the rehabilitation process by the strategic and skillful manipulation of environmental conditions, task sequences, and decision-making processes. One can only conclude that, as proudly as rehabilitation professionals sometimes exhibit their knowledge and successes, the entire field with all its disciplines is quite primitive and has its own special folklore which is comforting but does not promote the realization of optimal potential among our patients.

It must be conceded that very little is known, outside of the effects of actual CNS damage or sensory defects, of the effects of physical illnesses, disabilities, treatment, and training demands on the processes of attention, learning, and performance. However, it may be added that simply the processes of aging can introduce changes with which we must all contend in rehabilitation. Longitudinal and comparative studies with aging persons are in general agreement that significant decrements occur in perceptual, perceptual-motor, and intellectual functioning (Birren, 1959).

Rabbitt (1965) has indicated in summarizing comparative perceptual studies of young and aging subjects that, "The most general implication of all these data is that old subjects have difficulty in ignoring irrelevant or redundant information and are consequently at a disadvantage in searching amongst complex stimuli or learning to discriminate between patterns" (p. 47). On the other hand, no essential differences have been found, according to Davies and Griew (1965), in correlating age and performance at vigilance tasks. The impression of these authors and other experimenters is that typically older subjects in such experiments are more motivated to achieve greater output and to avoid errors than younger ones.

In studies of young and old experienced industrial workers (Murrell & Griew, 1965) it has been found that, "In so far as the experiments allowed the isolation of specific factors contributing to the overall decrement in performance, the actual times taken to make *movements* did not seem to differ much between young and old; rather the difference was in the times required for *decision-making* and *discrimination*" (p. 62). In studies of micrometer reading, for example, three groups of workers (age groups 20-34, 35-49, 50-64) showed a significantly progressive decrement in both speed and accuracy with increasing age.

Inglis (1965) has offered evidence that decrement in learning and performance in older subjects is primarily related to the decay in short-term memory and greater susceptibility to interference with aging, the effect, of course, being exaggerated with cerebral pathology. However, as Spieth (1965) has pointed out, the effects of aging per se must be isolated from the performance decrements arising from disease and disability.

In a series of studies employing psychological tests and perceptual-motor tasks, Spieth found the usual slower and poorer performance among older men but also confirmed further performance decrements among those with cardiovascular disease. His subjects included sizable groups of 1A and 1B (AHA standard classification) men for whom performance was significantly poorer than for age-control subjects. The favored explanation for these results was circulatory insufficiency to the central nervous system, especially in atherosclerosis and coronary artery disease and autnonomic dysfunction. Situational stresses and anxiety were ruled out as influencing the results, and differences were again in both speed and accuracy of performance.

In regard to other physiological variations, Sharp and Murphy (1965) have shown that performance decrements, characterized primarily by lethargy and increased reaction times, are also produced by uremia. They have shown comparable disruptions of a previously learned response by inducing uremia experimentally by nephrectomy and ureteral ligation and also by injections of human uremic material into animals.

Clinically, it has been noted that diabetic patients often have difficulty learning simple perceptual-motor tasks such as crutch gaits and in following exercise programs in physical therapy. This suggests that hypoglycemia may be the cause of decreased learning and performance decrements, an hypothesis which is confirmed by Clayson (1966). Behaviorally, hypoglycemia may result in a full gamut of effects ranging from lethargy, dullness, and somnolence to severe psychopathology and coma. McDaniel and Clayson (1966) have also demonstrated a depressing effect on the performance of coactors of hypoglycemic subjects. Hyperglycemia from induced diabetes, on the other hand (Clayson's 1966 study), actually enhanced the speed and accuracy of performance during learning over that of subjects with blood glucose levels within normal limits.

No doubt psychological research will continue to uncover limiting factors in behavior resulting from the many varied forms of human organic malfunction. The effects of structural and functional limitations upon human learning and performance is the least adequately understood area to date, and yet one of the most important. On the other hand, when more complex aspects of human performance are considered, as in occupational performance, there is abundant evidence from many surveys and follow-up studies that the physically disabled can train and perform perfectly satisfactorily at all occupational levels. The circumstances facilitating or precluding occupational performance by physically disabled, however, are not well clarified in spite of the many repeated studies which have been conducted. At best, it is typically concluded in many of these studies that performance in occupational or other complex situations depends upon such factors as age, education, previous experience and "motivation," which brings us back to our original problems. We will proceed now to an examination of occupational performance among the physically disabled, emphasizing research which has been concerned with actual functioning at work.

OCCUPATIONAL PERFORMANCE

The vocational adjustment of persons experiencing permanent physical limitations and changes in capacity is a matter of importance, although not exclusively a psychological question. Very simply put, with the occurrence of physical disability a limited number of economic outcomes are probable. One possibility is that the disabled person will once again become productively employable, self-sufficient, and able to provide for his own and his family's economic needs and security. On the other hand, we must also recognize the possibilities that the individual may for any number of reasons be supported as a dependent by his family or perhaps be maintained by the public through welfare or institutional resources. The latter outcomes are, of course, entirely undesirable from the standpoint of human resources and the values of American society and usually in the opinion of the disabled person himself.

There are many facets to the general problem of vocational adjustment of the physically disabled, and we have at hand a number of theories (McDaniel, 1963) which are of some value in understanding the general process of vocational choice and adjustment that most all persons, including those with physical impairments, go through. Vocational adjustment is a continuous process incorporating many individual changes, including physiological and psychological changes in functioning.

A great many surveys and follow-up studies have indicated that physically disabled persons are employed productively at a seemingly limitless range of occupations, with all types and degrees of physical limitations, and in spite of considerable reluctance by employers to hire them. The subject of the present discussion will, therefore, not be employability. This question is already answered. What can be determined concerning actual performance at work by physically disabled persons is chosen as a more psychologically appropriate question. Hence, the present discussion will be concerned primarily with *occupa-*

tional performance, rather than many other factors logically thought to be involved in the general process of vocational adjustment. At that, there are a great many variables which account for performance on the job.

The Industrial Relations Center of the University of Minnesota has, over the past several years, been concerned with the general problem of vocational adjustment of the disabled from a number of different angles. Recent studies (Carlson, Dawis, England & Lofquist, 1963) have focused on the questions of employment "satisfactoriness" or occupational performance. However, there are not many objective investigations of this type. Most research in vocational rehabilitation has reported only upon rates of employment or the types of employment of groups of disabled persons, without investigating their actual performance at work.

As examples of job cataloging studies which are interesting although telling us nothing about occupational performances, the Veterans Administration has in recent years published compilations of occupations and case reports for several disability groups. Two such reports (1957, 1960) concern occupations reported by Veterans Administration offices to be held by epileptic and paraplegic veterans, complete with interesting job descriptions for selected individuals. The distribution of occupations reported for these two disability groups are given on the following pages. Numbers in parentheses indicate the number of cases reported at each occupational level.

TABLE 7
SELECTED OCCUPATIONS OF EPILEPTIC VETERANS*

0–X   PROFESSIONAL, TECHNICAL AND
            MANAGERIAL WORK (178)
0–X1   ARTISTIC WORK   (3)
            0.2 Artistic Drawing and Related   (2)
            0.5 Artistic Arranging (1)
0–X2   MUSICAL WORK   (1)
            0.6 Musical Work, Instrumental   (1)
0–X3   LITERARY WORK   (3)
            0.5 Copy Writing and Journalism   (3)
0–X4   ENTERTAINMENT WORK   (3)
            0.2 Entertainment Work, Oral   (3)
0–X6   PUBLIC SERVICE WORK   (11)
            0.0 Instructive Service Work   (6)
            0.1 Social Service Work   (5)
0–X7   TECHNICAL WORK   (73)
            0.0 Laboratory Science Work   (12)
            0.1 Business Relations Work   (28)
            0.4 Engineering and Related   (23)
            0.7 Drafting and Related   (10)
0–X8   MANAGERIAL WORK   (84)
            0.1 Managerial Work, CAFS   (70)
            0.3 Managerial Work, Geographical   (14)
1–X   CLERICAL AND SALES WORK   (201)
1–X1   COMPUTING WORK   (7)
            0.1 Computing Work   (7)
1–X2   RECORDING WORK   (97)
            0.0 General Recording Work   (38)
            0.2 Typing   (2)
            0.8 Equipment and Material Checking   (52)
            0.9 Routine Recording Work   (5)
1–X4   GENERAL CLERICAL WORK   (39)
            0.0 Classifying and Related Work   (28)
            0.4 Clerical Machine Operating (n.e.c)   (3)
            0.9 Routine Clerical Work (n.e.c.)   (8)
1–X5   PUBLIC CONTACT WORK   (58)
            0.0 General Public Contact Work   (7)
            0.5 Selling   (42)
            0.7 Customer Service Work   (9)

*Occupations of Epileptic Veterans of World War II & Korean Conflict.
VA pamphlet 22-6, Vet. Adm., Wash., D.C., 1960.

2–X   SERVICE WORK   (26)
2–X1   COOKING   (4)
     0.2 Quantity Cooking   (4)
2–X5   PERSONAL SERVICE   (22)
     0.2 Food Serving and Related   (8)
     0.6 Adult Care   (12)
     0.9 Miscellaneous Personal Service Work   (2)
3–X   AGRICULTURE, MARINE AND
          FORESTRY WORK   (48)
3–X1   FARMING   (44)
     0.0 General Farming   (28)
     0.1 Animal Care   (3)
     0.2 Crop Farming   (13)
3–X8   MARINE WORK   (3)
     0.7 Navigation Work   (3)
3–X9   FORESTRY WORK   (1)
     0.9 Forest Work   (1)
4–X   MECHANICAL WORK   (163)
4–X2   MACHINE TRADES   (52)
     0.0 Machining   (7)
     0.1 Mechanical Repairing   (42)
     0.4 Complex Machine Operating (n.e.c.)   (3)
4–X6   CRAFTS   (111)
     0.1 Electrical Repairing   (17)
     0.2 Structural Crafts   (41)
     0.3 Bench Crafts   (36)
     0.5 Graphic Art Work   (9)
     0.6 Processing   (8)
6–X   MANUAL WORK   (126)
6–X2   OBSERVATIONAL WORK   (20)
     0.2 Structural Equipment Tending   (2)
     0.3 Inspecting and Testing   (7)
     0.4 Machine Tending (n.e.c.)   (7)
     0.6 Processing Equipment Tending   (4)
6–X4   MANIPULATIVE WORK   (34)
     0.2 Structural Work   (5)
     0.3 Bench Work, Assorted Materials   (21)
     0.4 Machine Operating, Manipulative   (7)
     0.6 Processing   (1)
6–X6   ELEMENTAL WORK   (72)
     0.1 Elemental Work, Light   (3)
     0.6 Elemental Work, Medium and Heavy   (69)

TABLE 8

SELECTED OCCUPATIONS OF PARAPLEGIC VETERANS*

0–X   PROFESSIONAL, TECHNICAL AND
       MANAGERIAL WORK   (224)
0–X1   ARTISTIC WORK   (14)
       0.2 Artistic Drawing and Related   (3)
       0.3 Artistic Shaping   (2)
       0.5 Artistic Arranging   (9)
0–X2   MUSICAL WORK   (2)
       0.6 Musical Work, Instrumental   (2)
0–X3   LITERARY WORK   (14)
       0.1 Creative Writing   (3)
       0.5 Copy Writing and Journalism   (11)
0–X4   ENTERTAINMENT WORK   (5)
       0.2 Entertainment Work, Oral   (4)
       0.9 Entertainment Work (n.e.c.)   (1)
0–X6   PUBLIC SERVICE WORK   (36)
       0.0 Instructive Service Work   (24)
       0.1 Social Service Work   (10)
       0.2 Protective Service Work   (2)
0–X7   TECHNICAL WORK   (77)
       0.0 Laboratory Science Work   (11)
       0.1 Business Relations Work and Related   (26)
            0.11 Accounting and Related Work   (8)
            0.12 Legal Work   (14)
            0.15 Purchase and Sales Work   (4)
       0.3 Geographical Science Work   (5)
       0.4 Engineering and Related   (16)
       0.7 Drafting and Related   (19)
0–X8   MANAGERIAL WORK   (76)
       0.10 Managerial Work (Clerical, Administrative Fiscal,
            Sales)   (62)
       0.31 Farming Supervision   (8)
       0.41 Managerial Work, Manufacturing   (4)
       0.49 Managerial Work, Transporation and
            Miscellaneous Services   (2)

*Occupations of Paraplegic Veterans of World War II & Korea.
VA Pamphlet 7-12, Vet. Adm., Wash., D.C., 1957

1—X   CLERICAL AND SALES WORK   (102)
1—X1   COMPUTING WORK   (7)
        0.1 Computing Work   (7)
1—X2   RECORDING WORK   (29)
        0.0 General Recording Work   (20)
        0.2 Typing (n.e.c.)   (4)
        0.8 Equipment and Material Checking   (3)
        0.9 Routine Recording Work   (2)
1—X4   GENERAL CLERICAL WORK   (8)
        0.0 Classifying and Related Work   (2)
        0.4 Clerical Machine Operating (n.e.c.)   (4)
        0.9 Routine Clerical Work (n.e.c.)   (2)
1—X5   PUBLIC CONTACT WORK   (58)
        0.0 General Public Contact Work   (19)
        0.5 Selling   (39)
3-X   AGRICULTURAL, MARINE AND
        FORESTRY WORK   (17)
3—X1   FARMING   (17)
        0.0 General Farming   (9)
        0.1 Animal Care   (6)
        0.2 Crop Farming   (2)
4—X   MECHANICAL WORK   (103)
4—X2   MACHINE TRADES   (12)
        0.1 Mechanical Repairing   (10)
        0.4 Complex Machine Operating (n.e.c.)   (2)
4—X6   CRAFTS   (91)
        0.1 Electrical Repairing   (10)
        0.2 Structural Crafts   (3)
        0.3 Bench Crafts   (59)
        0.5 Graphic Art Work   (19)
6—X   MANUAL WORK   (34)
6—X2   OBSERVATIONAL WORK   (3)
        0.3 Inspecting and Testing   (1)
        0.4 Machine Tending (n.e.c.)   (2)
6—X4   MANIPULATIVE WORK   (30)
        0.2 Structural Work   (1)
        0.3 Bench Work (Assembling and Related)   (27)
        0.4 Machine Operating, Manipulative   (2)
6—X6   ELEMENTAL WORK   (1)
        0.1 Elemental Work, Light   (1)

To continue with the questions of occupational performance, Carlson *et al.* (1963) have described occupational performance in terms of employment satisfactoriness in which they have included many factors representing the employer's view of the disabled person's functioning and work adjustment. According to these investigators' point of view, "satisfactoriness" is determined by the work organization and environment and, "is defined by the series of tasks which he must perform and the set of rules to which he must submit. The behavior of the individual within this 'environment' is the basis for the 'satisfactoriness' evaluations" (p. 5). It is pointed out that the employer essentially is paying for behavior which conforms to these specifications.

The assessment of occupational performance involves such aspects as productivity (quality and quantity of work) and efficiency (absences, lateness, accidents) in addition to others. Carlson *et al.* have chosen to measure work satisfactoriness in terms of these and other variables such as job suitability, promotability, and pay raises. In their research, the performance of 483 physically disabled workers was compared with 496 non-disabled co-workers at both skilled and unskilled, blue-collar and white-collar levels. The major results of this study were that physically disabled workers did not compare favorably with their non-disabled co-workers in terms of overall performance ratings or the quality of their work but were similar on other indexes of performance. Quality in this case involved supervisors' judgments of a unitary trait (equal, better or worse than others). Overall performance was measured by supervisory ratings of "overall competence, the effectiveness with which they perform their jobs, their proficiency, their overall value" (p. 8). It was also interesting in this research that job satisfaction and occupational performance were found to be independent and uncorrelated for both disabled and non-disabled workers. In all other aspects of occupational performance, including absenteeism, lateness, accidents, disciplinary actions, promotions and raises, the disabled did not differ significantly from their non-disabled co-workers.

The earliest and largest study of the occupational performance of physically disabled workers was one reported in 1948 by the United States Department of Labor. One finds this survey, entitled *The Performance of Physically Impaired Workers in Manufacturing Industries,* quoted extensively in the literature on vocational rehabilitation as evidence supporting the employability of the disabled. The research compared the performance records of over 11,000 physically impaired and over 18,000 unimpaired workers at 109 plants in 20 industrial manufacturing classifications. From the standpoint of sampling, then, one would expect this report to be a most reliable source of information even though specific comparisons (abseenteeism, injury rates, output, quit rates) were not made on the entire population sampled.

It was mentioned in the report of this survey that during World War II most manufacturing plants studied had relaxed physical standards for employment. However, after manpower shortages had eased, many of these same plants were found to have reinstated policies of excluding physically impaired workers. In only 25 of the 109 plants studied were there no exclusion policies of any sort for any type of physical impairment. The labor market condition at the time of the study was therefore a very special one created by wartime manpower shortages, and one which did not last much beyond a few years. However, the Department of Labor (1948) survey should still provide us some sound information concerning occupational performance. Only one qualification is necessary involving the types of physical impairments of the survey group (pp. 12-15). The only physical impairment reported for almost one-third of the entire group (32.1%) of over 11,000 impaired workers was hernia (3543 cases). This, of course, is a relatively mild impairment that is usually easily minimized. Outside of this largest impairment group there were 16.7% cardiac, 15.6% visual,

13.8% orthopedic, and 5.3% multiple physical impairments. Small proportions of peptic ulcer, diabetes, tuberculosis, hearing loss, and epilepsy were also included.

Although the statistical significance of the findings of this early survey was not reported by the Department of Labor, the conclusion was reached that, "Analysis of the data shows conclusively that the physically impaired person was not necessarily a handicapped worker. When given reasonable job placement consideration, that is, the individual's abilities balanced against the job requirements, the physically impaired workers as a group were fully able to compete successfully with unimpaired workers similarly placed" (p. 3). Other general conclusions were that physically impaired workers were quite similar to unimpaired workers doing the same jobs in terms of absenteeism, injury rates, and relative productivity. The only major difference detected by this survey was in respect to separations from employment. Both voluntary separations (quit rate) and terminations were considerably higher for the physically impaired group based on records of 5217 impaired and 8783 unimpaired workers. Unfortunately, complete data were not provided for every comparison of occupational performance for each class of impaired workers and non-impaired controls.

An additional few studies of minor significance to the present discussion may also be mentioned. Wyshak, Snegineff, and Law (1961) reported a study of the work experience of 709 persons with cardiovascular disease or diabetes compared with 709 matched controls free from these diseases. Subjects engaged in a variety of occupations, from sedentary to heavy labor, employed in the Boston and New York areas. The analysis of work experience included absence experience, utilization of medical facilities, sickness and workmen's compensation benefits. In all, 1418 persons from 18 companies were included in the study. Persons identified were matched with controls within each firm, the disabled group including 653 cardiac and 56 diabetic employees.

Wyshak, *et al.* found that the disabled group lost significantly more work days than controls. Average days lost per year were 13.9 and 7.5 respectively. The number of days lost per incident was also higher for the study group. Far higher absentee rates and lost time in specific company studies have also been reported for cardiacs (Franco, 1954; Thompson & Huntington, 1956) and for diabetics (Nasr, Block & Magnuson, 1966) by other investigators. During the year of study by Wyshak, *et al.* none of the cardiovascular disease cases had workmen's compensation claims for work-connected cardiac episodes. The conclusion was reached that, "Although, on the basis of the findings of this study it cannot be said that in terms of work experience persons with cardiovascular disease compare favorably with their counterparts who are free from cardiovascular disease, the results indicate that cardiacs can and do work" (p. 221).

Jaffe, Day, and Adams (1964) have published a recent study designed to examine the work experiences of a number of seriously and permanently disabled workmen and to determine empirically what occurs insofar as their subsequent employment was concerned. Nearly 1300 industrially injured workmen in the New York metropolitan area were interviewed to determine their employment histories and current labor force status, and although not directly concerned with actual occupational performance, the study presents some interesting results. Jaffe, *et al.* summarized their findings as follows: "We may apply these criteria as follows: (a) select out all men with chain injuries; (b) of the remainder, select out those aged 45 and over and who had only eight years or less of schooling" (p. 23). According to the authors, this will take out about half the population of disabled men, including about four-fifths of all the future job failures and marginal adjustments. These would be the men who would be in need of rehabilitation services to improve their vocational adjustment. Successful employment adjustment following injury has been equated by Jaffe, *et al.* in large part to returning to the same employer and occupation, "The character of the first job obtained by the injured worker upon reentry into the labor force was an excellent indication of future labor market activities—at least for the next five years or so. If the disabled worker returned to work for the same firm for which he had worked at the time of injury and to the same occupation, he was most likely to have a good job five years later. On the other hand, if he found employment with a different firm or changed occupation, he was more likely to have a poor job— or no job—five years later" (p. 22).

Studies of the performance of physically disabled persons engaged in specific occupations are rare and very much needed. One recent contribution by King (1965) reports on the occupational performance of physically disabled public school teachers. Information was collected from school principals concerning the performance of 431 handicapped teachers. It was found that teachers who were blind, deaf, or who had severe problems in ambulation were most affected by their impairments in this occupation. The teaching tasks reported most influenced by physical impairments were, however, non-classroom activities such as field trips, study hall and lunchroom supervision, and other disciplinary functions.

In a descriptive study of the visually handicapped in professional, sales, and managerial work, Bauman (1963) elaborates numerous characteristics of this group including demographic data, educational factors, counseling obtained, professional work experience, and attitudes. It was based on field interview data with 434 persons who were successful in the professions or in business, 91 of whom were women and 343 men. Relationships are reported in the form of frequency distributions and cross tabulations which were held to have some statistical or experiential significance.

Among the observations made by this author were that these successfully employed persons were well-educated, well-counseled, and had generally favorable attitudes towards their blindness, training, employment, and counseling. The author states in conclusion, "Shall we not conclude, then, that none of the characteristics we can count, such as amount of vision, amount of education, cause of visual loss, etc., makes the difference between success and failure? If it were possible (and we very much wish it were possible) to study an equal number of blind persons who have not succeeded, we would probably find the same proportions with these basic life characteristics" (p. 98). It was observed that success was gained primarily through persistence and effort in dealing with employer's attitudes.

In yet another type of study with marginal bearing upon the question of occupational performance of the physically disabled, Lunde and Bigman (1959) have reported some information concerning occupational stability among the deaf. Their results, based on mailed survey responses of 10,101 deaf persons revealed that, "Over two-thirds of the deaf who had been employed had held only one job in the preceding ten years (67.8%). Only about a fifth had held three or more different jobs in the decade. This appears to indicate very great stability" (p. 29). Job stability among the employed deaf was substantiated by length of time on the job, and job satisfaction reports would also seem to bear this out. Although this research does not provide information concerning actual performance on the job, it does suggest, at least, that the deaf who are employed are quite stable workers.

Another most interesting collection of information concerning occupational performance has been provided by Campbell, Leizer, and Yuker (1959) based upon the experiences of Abilities, Inc., a New York electronics company which hires *only* physically disabled workers. The principal value of the report lies in the illustrations of many job and equipment adaptations which have made possible industrial employment with many types of impairments in many different operations. Apparently, the company's experience in production, absenteeism, and injury rates has been a satisfactory one.

Felton, Spencer, and Chappell (1959) have reported findings concerning the occupational performance of 3657 civilian employees of the Air Force who were designated as physically disabled. The impairments of this sample varied considerably in type and severity with the largest proportions working in occupations related to the maintenance of aircraft, engines and related equipment, and in control, distribution, and storage of parts and equipment. Comparisons of the records of physically disabled workers were made with non-disabled doing the same work in the same departments.

In contrast to a study previously mentioned (Carlson, *et al.*), not only were certain differences in occupational performances among physically disabled employees and their non-disabled co-workers found, but a relation with job satisfaction was also obtained for both groups. Felton, *et al.* have thus concluded, "In handicapped and non-handicapped alike, job effectiveness of the dissatisfied was inferior to that of the satisfied workers, as measured by all indices of worker effectiveness used in the study. The differences between satisfied and dissatisfied workers were, however, much greater among the handicapped, indicating that morale among the handicapped had a greater influence on their effectiveness as workers than it did on the non-handicapped" (p. 221).

TABLE 9

MEAN DIFFERENCES BETWEEN SATISFIED
AND DISSATISFIED* EMPLOYEES IN
SIX INDICES OF WORKER EFFECTIVENESS

	Handicapped		
Indices	Satis-fied Means	Dissat-isfied Means	Differ-ences
Illness-absence rate	4.78	6.90	2.12
Accident rate	0.58	1.01	0.43
Dispensary visit rate	3.47	5.94	2.47
% receiving commendations	54.00	33.00	21.00
% receiving reprimands	22.00	33.00	11.00
Promotion rate	0.36	0.29	0.07
	Non-handicapped		
Illness-absence rate	3.19	3.64	0.45
Accident rate	0.46	0.58	0.12
Dispensary visit rate	3.18	4.68	1.50
% receiving commendations	54.00	33.00	21.00
% receiving reprimands	11.00	42.00	31.00
Promotion rate	0.30	0.28	0.02

*From Felton, Spencer & Chappell, 1959.

The above table presents differences between handicapped-non-handicapped, satisfied-dissatisfied workers in the study by Felton, *et al.* Differences between the findings of these investigators and those of Carlson *et al.* (1963) in the relation of job satisfaction to performance among physically disabled workers is not, however, unusual. Much contradictory evidence is found in industrial psychology (Vroom, 1964) concerning this issue. Vroom has concluded that probably the two variables are independent, but feels that the effects of actual job performance upon satisfaction is as important as the reverse effect. Clearly, this is a complex relationship. Vroom hypothesizes:

The effects of performance on a task or work role on satisfaction with that role varies with the extent to which performance is relevant to the worker's self-conception. If a person believes that a task requires abilities which he values and believes himself to possess, then success will be consonant with his self-concept and accompanied by satisfaction; whereas failure will be disconsonant with his self-concept and accompanied by dissatisfaction. On the other hand, if he believes that the task does not require any abilities which he values and believes himself to possess, then his level of performance will be irrelevant to his self-concept (p. 147).

Felton, Spencer, and Chappell's (1959) results indicated that their dissatisfied handicapped workers most frequently expressed their grievances in terms of their physical disabilities. In this report, failure to progress, to achieve higher salaries, to obtain more interesting work, were related by these workers to personal inadequacy resulting from physical disability, indicating some relationship with the worker's self-conceptions.

More general findings of the study by Felton, *et al.*, confirm that on most measures physically disabled workers performed as well or better than their non-disabled co-workers. The disabled achieved promotions at a significantly faster rate than non-disabled workers in the same occupation for a comparable length of service. As a group, however, the disabled employees also had significantly higher illness-absence rates and accident rate. Felton, *et al.* have thus concluded, "General findings in the analyses of the various indices of worker effectiveness point to strengths, weaknesses, and problems of the handicapped worker" (p. 220). The same conclusion is appropriate, furthermore, for all of the research available to date concerning occupational performance by the physically disabled.

Research in the vocational adjustment of the physically disabled has progressed only a short distance beyond the question of employability. However, there is now ample demonstration of employability and we may safely assume that physically dis-

tions. The more vital and incompletely answered question is how well do the physically disabled perform their jobs in comparison with their non-disabled co-workers.

TABLE 10

SUMMARY OF OCCUPATIONAL
PERFORMANCE STUDIES

Major studies	Absentee rates	Injury rates	Production	Stability	Quality of work
Carlson et al. (1963)	no difference	no difference	no difference	no difference	disabled poorer
U. S. Dept. Labor (1948)	no difference	no difference	no difference	disabled poorer	
Felton et al. (1959)	disabled poorer	disabled poorer	no difference	no difference	no difference

Here the objective evidence is somewhat inconsistent and in great need of further clarification. However, the weight of comparisons now available appear to favor the tentative conclusion that physically disabled workers do not differ significantly from their non-disabled co-workers in overall occupational performance. If we summarized the results of the three largest and most comprehensive studies now available (Carlson et al., 1963; U.S. Dept. Labor, 1948; Felton et al., 1959), we find that in only four out of fourteen comparisons were the physically disabled found to be inferior workers to their non-disabled counterparts. No other differences in these three major investigations were statistically significant, which is to be appreciated in considering that in all three studies combined, over 15,000 physically disabled workers were studied as to their actual performance on the job. It must be remembered, however, that we can only accept these data as suggestive, at present, for even among the three major studies there is a great deal of disturbing inconsistency in their findings.

References

Andrews, J.   Neuromuscular reeducation of the hemiplegic with the aid of the electromyograph. *Arch. PM&R*, 1964, **45**, 530-2.

Basmajian, J., Baeza, M. & Fabrigar, C.   Conscious control and training of individual spinal motor neurons in normal human subjects. *J. New Drugs*, 1965, **5**, 78-85.

Bilodeau, I. Information feedback. In *Acquisition of Skill* (Bilodeau, Ed.), Academic Press, New York, 1966.

Birch, H., Belmont, I. & Karp, E.   Excitation-inhibition balance in brain-damaged patients. *J. Nerv. Ment. Dis.*, 1964, **139**, 537-44.

Birch, H., Belmont, I. & Karp, E.   The prolongation of inhibition in brain-damaged patients. *Cortex*, 1965, 1, 397-409.

Birch, H., Belmont, I. & Karp, E.   Delayed information processing and extinction following cerebral damage. *Brain*, 1967, **90**, 113-30.

Birren, J. Sensation, perception, and modification of behavior in relation to the process of aging. In *The Process of Aging in the Nervous System.* (Birren, Imus & Windle, Eds.) Thomas, Springfield, Ill., 1959.

Campbell, W., Leizer, R. & Yuker, H. *A Study of the Adaptability of Disabled Workers.* Hum. Res. Study No. 3, 1959, Hum. Res. Corp., Albertson, N.Y.

Carlson, R., Dawis, R., England, G. & Lofquist, L. *The Measurement of Employment Satisfactoriness.* Minn. Studies in Voc. Rehab., XIV, 1963, University of Minnesota.

Cernacek, J.   Contralateral motor irradiation-cerebral dominance. *Arch. Neurol.*, 1961, **4**, 165-72.

Clayson, S.   Effect of hypoglycemia on T-maze learning in rats. Unpublished thesis, 1966, University of Colorado.

Davies, D. & Griew, S. Age and vigilance. In *Behavior, Aging, and the Nervous System.* (Welford & Birren, Ed.) 1965. Thomas, Springfield, Ill.

Felton, J., Spencer, C. & Chappell, J. *Work Relationships of the Physically Impaired in a Multiple Disability Sheltered Workshop and in Standard Industry.* 1959, Final report, Proj. 110, Univ. Okla. Med. Cent., Oklahoma City.

Franco, S. The cardiac can work. *Indust. Med. & Surg.*, 1954, **23**, 315-20.

Goodkin, R. Improved verbal and motor behavior of hemiplegics by operant conditioning. (Abstr.). *Amer. Psychologist,* 1966, **21,** 621.

Hellebrandt, F. Cross education: Ipsilateral and contralateral effects of unimanual training. *J. Appl. Physiol.*, 1951, **4**, 136-44.

Ince, L. Sokolow, J. & Menon, M. Escape and avoidance conditioning of responses in the plegic arm of stroke patients. (Abstr.). *Amer. Psychologist,* 1966, **21,** 620.

Inglis, J. Immediate memory, age and brain function. In *Behavior, Aging, and the Nervous System* (Welford & Birren, Eds.) 1965. Thomas, Springfield, Ill.

King, G. The incidence of employed New Jersey public school teachers having certain physical handicaps and the effect of the handicap on specific teaching tasks. (Abstr.) *Rehab. Lit.*, 1965, **26**, p. 345.

Louttit, R. A bibliography in neuropsychology. Reviews and books 1960-1965. *Publ. Hlth, Serv. Pub. No. 1473*, 1966.

Lunde, A. & Bigman, S. *Occupational Conditions Among the Deaf.* 1959, Gallaudet College, Washington, D.C.

Madison, H. & Herring, M. An experimental study of motivation. *Amer. J. Occup. Ther.*, 1960, **14**, 253-5.

McDaniel, J.   Disability and vocational redevelopment. *J. Rehab.*, 1963, **29**, 16-18.

McDaniel, J. & Clayson, S.   Social facilitation of a previously learned response in normal, hypoglycemic, and alloxan diabetic rats. *Psychonom. Sci.*, 1967, **6**, 499-500.

Murrell, K. & Griew, S. Age, experience and speed of response. In *Behavior, Aging, and the Nervous System.* (Welford & Birren, Eds.) 1965, Thomas, Springfield, Ill.

Nasr, A., Block, D. & Magnuson, H.   Absenteeism experience in a group of employed diabetics. *J. Occup. Med.*, 1966, **8**, 621-5.

Posner, M. Components of skilled performance. *Science*, 1966, **152**, 1712-18.

Rabbitt, P. Age and discrimination between complex stimuli. In *Behavior, Aging, and the Nervous System.* (Welford & Birren, Eds.) 1965, Thomas, Springfield, Ill.

Sharp, J. & Murphy, G.   A behavioral bioassay method of using material from a uremic patient. *Percept. Mot. Skills*, 1966, **22**, 127-33.

Simard, T. & Basmajian, J.   Methods in training the conscious control of motor units. *Arch. PM&R*, 1967, **48**, 12-19.

Smith, A. & Burklund, C.   Nondominant hemispherectomy: Neuropsychological implications for human brain function. *Proceed. Amer. Psychol. Assoc.*, 1967, **2**, 103-04.

Smith, A. & Burklund, C.   Dominant hemispherectomy: Preliminary report on neuropsychological sequelae. *Science*, 1966, **153**, 1280-2.

Smith, K. & Henry, J. Cybernetic Foundations of Rehabilitation Science. University of Wisconsin, 1966 (mimeo).

Smith, K.   Cybernetic theory and analysis of learning. In *Acquisition of Skill.* (Bilodeau, Ed.) 1966 Academic Press, New York.

Spieth, W. Slowness of task performance and cardiovascular diseases. In *Behavior, Aging, and the Nervous System.* (Welford & Birren, Eds.) 1965, Thomas, Springfield, Ill.

Taub, E., Bacon, R. & Berman, A. Acquisition of a trace conditioned avoidance response after deafferentation of the responding limb. *J. Comp. Physiol. Psychol.*, 1965, **59**, 275-9.

Taub, E., Ellman, S. & Berman, A. Deafferentation in monkeys: Effect on conditioned grasp response. *Science*, 1966, **151**, 593-4.

Thompson, W. & Huntington, C. The cardiac strikes oil. *Indust. Med. & Surg.*, 1956, **25**, 463-5.

Trombly, C. Principles of operant conditioning: Related to orthotic training of quadriplegic patients. *J. Occup. Ther.*, 1966, **20**, 217-20.

U. S. Dept. Labor. The performance of physically impaired workers in manufacturing industries. 1948, *Bull. No. 923,* Bur. Labor Stat., Washington, D.C.

Van Buskirk, C. Return of motor function in hemiplegia. *Neurol.*, 1954, **4**, 919-28.

Veterans Administration. *Occupations of Paraplegic Veterans of World War II & Korean Conflict.* VA pamphlet 7-12, 1957, VA, Wash. D.C.

Veterans Administration. *Occupations of Epileptic Veterans of World War II & Korea.* VA pamphlet 22-6, 1960, VA, Wash., D.C.

Vroom, V. *Work and Motivation.* 1964, Wiley, New York.

Chapter VII

SUMMARY AND THEORETICAL CONSIDERATIONS

THE SCOPE of this volume is somewhat limited because of two factors. One, the admitted selectivity with which information has been chosen for inclusion, the judgment having been made to include only the most reliable experimental evidence available. Clinical reports, case studies, statements of opinion or philosophy, and descriptive reports were excluded as a matter of policy, even though such information is definitely instructive for certain purposes. Two, the paucity of the "hard" data testifies to the fact that the "State of the Art" concerning the behavioral effects of structural and functional changes resulting from illness and disability is a rather primitive state indeed. I believe that we owe this regrettable state of limited knowledge to the fact that experimentally oriented researchers have not been interested in the problems of physical disability, leaving the definition and exploration of the problems to those of a psychopathological approach which has produced something of a "defectology", to use current Russian terminology. The psychopathological approach to physical disability has not only been fruitless, it has been retarding the development of scientific psychological study of the problems of physical disabilities and rehabilitation. It is true that our studies have suffered from the lack of a logical, concise statement of what to look for, even the popular conceptions of somatopsychology not having been designed nor experienced to be very definitive of the problems in question. Recently, in trying to explain this to sympathizers and skeptics alike, Shontz (1965) has stated:

> A review of the sources from which this important concept arose reveals that these developments are not prescribed by any formal definition of the subject. Indeed, careful study of the matter establishes that somatopsychology is not identified with any particular theoretical point of view and it does not deal exclusively with the effects of atypical or pathological somatic conditions. Despite the apparent implications of its name, it does not propose to explain psychological events in somatic terms; and it is by no means an alternate expression for 'rehabilitation psychology' (p. 20).

Probably the most promising step taken toward filling the void of an organized theory and logical statement of the psychological effects of structural and functional changes is that being advanced by Karl U. Smith in terms of "Neurogeometric" or cybernetic principles of behavior. Since neither social psychological nor psychopathological approaches have proved entirely satisfactory in themselves, we, as students of human behavior seeking to understand the effects of disease and injury upon more global aspects of behavior, must feel obligated to look for more substantive and enlightening approaches to our questions. Hopefully, by bringing together evidence from many diverse sources for the first time, this volume will have aided in the search.

Preceding sections have been concerned with an evaluation of research involving the organization, and disruption of organization, of behavior as related to chronic illness and physical disability, treatment, and ultimately rehabilitation. These discussions might have been written as one rather than several since none of the phenomena are distinct psychological processes. They merely serve as convenient though arbitrary and artificial categories of behavior that are interrelated systems in a vastly complex process of behavior regulation and control. The precise integration of these systems is still admittedly unclear, as are many of the neurophysiological substrates which serve them. Nevertheless, a somewhat different frame of reference based upon the assumption of a central regulating and controlling process has been employed in the sections. We have been concerned with the process itself, of course, but more specifically with what is currently known about the influences of structural and functional limitations and changes in the body upon this process and its mechanisms.

The primary initial assumption is that the effective organization and control of behavior requires several intact, contributing mechanisms. Any structural or functional change in the organism may disrupt temporarily or permanently these mechanisms, thereby affecting the self-regulating, self-correcting process of behavior regulation and control. The function of all of the technologies of treatment and rehabilitation are, from this standpoint, to correct and restore the individual's capacity for effective behavior control. Psychologically, the following scheme may be useful in understanding this point of view.

Effective behavior control and regulation require fundamental systems having certain common properties. The central process involves the functions of (1) selecting and processing information, (2) organization and directional guidance, (3) activation of appropriate mechanisms, (4) acquisition and modification of means of organization and control, and (5) the storage and retrieval of information and control patterns. All of these have the common properties of being (a) mutually dependent, each interactive and dependent upon the others; (b) specialized and selective, being not only specialized functions, but being highly selective in input-output operations; (c) intrinsically controlled by the organism itself and largely independent of external control; (d) excitatory and inhibitory, activating essential units while damping non-essential.

Mechanisms of sensation, perception, attention, feedback, habituation and others serve the system for selecting and processing information. Input is highly selective and the system

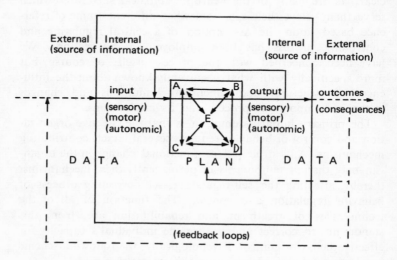

Fig. 7.   Schematic representation of the process of central regulation and control of behavior.

Necessary Functions

A. Selection and processing of information.
B. Organization and directional guidance.
C. Activation of appropriate mechanisms.
D. Acquisition and modification of means of control.
E. Storage and retrieval of information and control patterns.

Properties

1. mutually dependent, interactive.
2. specialized and selective in input-output.
3. intrinsically controlled.
4. graded responses.
5. excitatory and inhibitory components.

has various means and levels of modulation available. The selection and processing of information are influenced quite directly by other systems, especially in that only information is selected and processed for which the system is "prepared" or programmed.

Concepts such as motivation, attitudes, values and expectations belong to the system for organization and directional guidance. Observed or inferred individual differences are fundamentally differences in direction and magnitude, although intraindividual differences in magnitude, i.e., graded responses, are often our principal concern. Patterns of organization and the direction of behavior are intrinsically controlled by the organism independent of direct external control; the organization of complex human behavior is not stimulus-response controlled. Certain aspects of organization have already been shown to be controlled by specialized neurophysiological mechanisms, but simply establishing the organization or direction that behavior will take is not sufficient to account for output in terms of responses or activity. Activating or arousal mechanisms, including concepts such as emotion and drive, are important from the standpoint of directed activity and particularly in potentiating the activity of all relevant systems of behavior regulation and control. At the same time, it is apparent that neither under-activation nor excessive arousal facilitate effective performance even with appropriate information and organization. There is evidence that organizational patterns operate primarily to reduce the perceptual thresholds for appropriate information which in turn activates or triggers the behavior consistent with the imposed organization.

In addition to the selection and processing of information, organization, directional guidance, and activating systems, there is needed a system for the acquisition and modification of means of regulation and control. This defines the concept of "learning," which obviously depends upon the functioning of the other systems. All learning is instrumental by the definition just given. Finally, of course, a system for the storage and retrieval is absolutely necessary, for without "memory" there can be no effective regulation and control of behavior.

Although this conception may seem highly mechanistic at first glance, I believe that it is not much different, even though much more specific, than the conception of human behavior expressed by the eminent theorist and psychotherapist, Carl Rogers, in his prolific writings. The inherent plasticity of the human organism in maintaining and enhancing intrinsic qualities of self-regulation and self-correction should be our point of departure. Recognizing this principle, it should be our objective to discover what may happen to the organism to disrupt self-regulating and controlling processes, and to discover the means of restoring or correcting the individual's capacities to control and determine his own behavior. In the belief that structural and functional limitations are important in determining the individual's capacity for self-regulation and control, scientific investigation of such changes is an obvious necessity. Furthermore, it should be clear that any inferences which professionals make with authority about what behavior on the part of a patient or client may be desirable, beneficial, or essential are apt to be largely irrelevant in terms of intrinsic regulation and control. Structural and functional changes resulting from disease or injury may be adventitious or the result of the person's own negligence or even design. The cause is not as important to the present problems as the specific effects.

It is quite clear that psychological studies must make greater application of such behavioral mechanisms as those of attention, arousal, and others which are intrinsic control mechanisms and have recently been rather well defined by many investigators. In the belief that such factors must increasingly be taken into account in much of patient care and rehabilitation at some time in the near future, some background can be supplied. Hopefully, the following discussion will suggest some clinical and research applications of what has been demonstrated to occur within the central nervous system, and behaviorally as well, during information processing, which it must always be borne in mind has excitatory *and* inhibitory components.

An encouraging report of the clinical application of principles of attention, conscious awareness, and habituation has recently been made by Gootzeit (1965) to work with severely retarded and brain injured patients. The primary assumption of this report is correctly made that, "Social and psychological interrelationships and communication are dependent on the state of awareness during which the mechanisms of focus, attention, and habituation are utilized to arrive at a readiness to communicate and interrelate" (p. 161). Applications should not be limited to these disabilities, however, since we will be considering the mechanisms of normal perceptual and learning processes.

Just as the focusing of attention may be thought of as an excitatory process in perception and learning, we must also have *habituation* as the attenuation or "screening-out" of irrelevant, extraneous stimulation which would interfere with performance. There are a number of different viewpoints concerning habituation, most of which seem to have given recognition to only one or another aspect of the process. Apparently there have been three basic theoretical positions represented in learning theories and in neurophysiology which are best designated as exhaustive, inhibitory, and anticipatory. Representing the exhaustive school of thought are the notions of Skinner (1938, 1957), Mowrer (1960), and Montgomery (1954, 1955), who believe that the arousing effects of novel stimulation gradually become exhausted and adapt or extinguish as a result of reflex fatigue. On the other hand, there are those who make an inhibitory interpretation, notably Pavlov (1927), Sokolov (1960, 1963), and Gastaut (1957, 1958). Supported by extensive research on central nervous system activities during habituation and classical conditioning, the inhibitory position fundamentally states that habituation is the result of a blocking effect in the receptor pathways or a concentration of inhibition within the central nervous system. Finally, there is the view that habituation represents an anticipatory process of efferent responses acting upon receptor systems to control irrelevant sensory input. The supporters of this view have been Hernandez-Peon (1961), Hernandez-Peon and Scheerer (1955), Hernandez-Peon, Scheerer, and Jouvet (1956), Galambos, Sheatz, and Vernier (1956), Galambos (1956), and Sharpless and Jasper (1956). These neurophysiologists consider habituation to be a form of learning, or more specifically, "negative learning."

A recent review by Martin (1964) of the process of adaptation has considered the various meanings of the terms "adaptation" and "habituation" and would prefer combining the two processes under the generic term of "response decrement." While there is no question that both adaptation and habituation result in response decrement, no real understanding can result from such an oversimplification. In fact, Martin herself states, "It seems to be commonly accepted that the categories of adaptation and habituation are different . . ." (p. 39). Martin's review discusses the topic of adaptation from many points of view and only partly as related to response decrement. While there is merit in attempting to overcome semantic confusion, certain important issues must not be obscured. Martin has made one observation of significance which is, "These arguments for discriminating adaptation and habituation processes are basically concerned with learned versus non-learned responses" (p. 39).

Psychological learning theorists (Mowrer, 1960; Skinner, 1938) have conceived habituation as a process of the elimination of emotional behavior which must take place before learning can effectively occur. There have been few systematic attempts in learning theory to accommodate the phenomenon of habituation, but it has been superficially approached under a number of different concepts by several theorists. B. F. Skinner has applied the label of "adaptation" as follows: "(1) As operation: exposing an organism to a stimulus. (2) As process: a change in the extent of the reaction of the organism to the stimulus" (1957, p. 723). That this sort of conception is clearly inadequate has been explained by Sharpless and Jasper (1956) who state, "Habituation differs from both sensory adaptation and nerve accommodation in its temporal characteristics; it develops even when many minutes intervene between successive presentations of the stimulus and may persist for hours or even days." Furthermore, these authors, who have studied the process more closely than many others, have stated that, "It does not depend on effector fatigue, since a response which has become habituated to a specific stimulus may still be elicited by an appropriate novel stimulus, whereas a fatigued effector will fail to respond, not only to the repeated stimulus, but to all other stimuli of the same relative intensity" (p. 43).

The idea of the "novel stimulus" is the key to the whole process of habituation. Another contemporary learning theorist, O. H. Mowrer, has observed, "Preliminary observations had indicated that if animals were placed in a maze without prior habituation, they showed considerable anxiety. This was first indicated by great cautiousness of movement and excessive urination and defecation. Later there was a period of feverish exploration, during which the animals ignored food even though they had not eaten for 24-26 hours" (1960, p. 175). Whereas Skinner (1938, 1957) had explained the process of habituation in terms of "adapting out" emotional behavior, Mowrer has explicitly tied it to the reduction of fear. In neither of these is there to be found a recognition of the role of novelty or novel stimulation. Some others, however, have made steps in this direction.

The effects of novel stimulation have been the basis for several studies by various authors (Montgomery, 1955; Harlow, 1950, Butler, 1953) and have been attributed variously to an "exploratory drive" or "manipulative drive." Butler, for example, has found that monkeys learned object discrimina-ation at a high level of performance with novel stimulation as a reinforcer, i.e., being allowed to look out of the experimental apparatus through a small door for thirty seconds. This he attributed to an exploratory drive. Harlow has obtained similar results in studying the learning of monkeys of a complex puzzle without benefit of an extrinsic reward. Rhesus monkeys were given a puzzle to manipulate on 60 two-hour sessions for twelve days, and on the thirteenth day were given one hun-dred trials at six-minute intervals. Harlow had previously demon-strated learning under such conditions of "intrinsic motivation," and it is interesting to note the persistence of performance through one hundred presentations on a single day of brief intervals of repetition. Harlow found that the number of at-tacks on the puzzle remained relatively constant, but that manipulation of the object decreased rapidly during the day. It seems, therefore, that the animals gradually became habitu-ated to this source of novel stimulation. There is no apparent emotional component in these findings, but they are attributed to an intrinsic motivation.

Additional information comes from a series of investigations by Montgomery (1954, 1955) who was interested in determin-ing whether fear or an exploratory drive is responsible for the effects of novel stimulation. When rats were given access to a maze from their living cages, it was found that there was an increase in exploration over trials under various degrees of fear provoking conditions. Montgomery has reported, "The decrease in strength of fear evoked by novel stimuli is proportional to the amount of direct contact with such stimuli" (1955, p. 257).

Throughout the experimental and theoretical work in learn-ing, there is no definite conclusion to be reached concerning the ultimate nature of the habituation process. Psychological theories have made some contribution but, in general, have only con-sidered the emotional aspects of the process and oversimplified the effects of novel stimulation. Only recently has Pribram

(1963) produced a conception applied directly to the psychology of memory and cognition.

Obviously, such a pervasive mechanism as habituation has implications for many areas of application. Recently (McBain, 1961), the application of the more well-known aspects of habituation in regard to human performance have been indirectly approached experimentally. This research suggests that performance on an extremely monotonous task can be changed as a function of the variability of background stimuli: performance being poorer, i.e., lower productivity and greater errors in a constantly quiet background, and higher in moderately variable surroundings. In order to produce variability with low intelligibility, McBain used a sound source of noise capable of maintaining a moderate level of arousal in his subjects; his hypothesis being that such a degree of arousal should lead to optimal performance, while lower or higher arousal levels would be associated with reduced effectiveness. This is, interestingly, in opposition to the thinking of modern learning theorists such as Estes (1950) who tend to look upon all ambient sources of stimulation as competing stimuli and a hindrance to learning. McBain has recognized, in effect, that since all sensory inputs are routed to the nonspecific arousal system, any environmental change, including changes in auditory stimulation, should result in increased arousal. He also calls upon sensory deprivation studies to illustrate the impairment in behavior that results when environmental stimulation is severely restricted. It was found from this investigation that the increase in stimulus variability, which was brought about by the noise, acted uniformly throughout the experiment to significantly reduce the proportion of errors. The author's interpretation is, of course, that a moderate degree of arousal is necessary for the maintenance of the desired behavior. However, in terms of the mechanism of habituation, it can also be interpreted that under circumstances of stimulus variability the process does not occur, at least not completely. Stimuli in these conditions are unpredictable to the organism and, therefore, cannot be attenuated or dampened.

As mentioned earlier, contemporary learning theories have contributed little to the ultimate understanding of the process of habituation. It has been confused with fatigue, adaptation, and the extinction of fear. Mowrer (1960), for example, has interpreted his own observations as follows:

> Here the assumption is that hungry rats in an unfamiliar maze may, quite understandably, want to make sure that they are safe before they attempt to sate their hunger. Only after they are 'satisfied' that there is *nothing dangerous* in the new situation are they able, it seems, to respond to their nutritional needs. Although the fear is here, to be sure, elicited by stimulation external to the organism, there is no reason for assuming that it is any the less internal than is the metabolic drive of hunger (p. 175).

> The biological utility of such a tendency is clear; it is important for living organisms to know whether a given event is accidental or is associated in some orderly and predictable way with a particular place or action (p. 176).

This description shows only a vague conviction that the organism learns from novel stimulation and indicates the place of predictability of the occurrence of stimulus event in habituation. However, it must be recalled that it is only very recently that the phenomenon of habituation has become the object of controlled scientific inquiry. Furthermore, the refinement of the techniques of investigation, especially in neurophysiology, has made possible the isolation of many of the characteristics of habituation which heretofore have been attributed to other variables such as fear or reflex fatigue. The notion of fatigue, however, has not been done away with entirely and is presently favored by some neurophysiologists who have investigated the process.

In the first controlled experimental study of habituation, read before the seventy-fourth meeting of the American Physiological Society, Hernandez-Peon and Scheerer (1955) reported that they considered habituation to be simple learning not to respond to stimuli which tend to be insignificant for the organism. This phenomenon had been studied by means of microelectrodes implanted in the cochlear nucleus and the evoked potentials to acoustic stimuli recorded from unanesthetized, unrestrained cats. By the repetition of clicks at intervals of two seconds, it was demonstrated that after a variable number of trials the evoked potential disappeared or was greatly diminished. Furthermore, this attenuation was found to be selective for the particular repeated auditory stimulus and was not effective for a novel tone. Hernandez-Peon and Scheerer interpreted their evidence to indicate that the brain stem reticular formation was responsible for this selective, tonic, inhibitory influence. Other investigators have subsequently found that this assumption is true in part, at least in regard to the physiological mechanisms. All agree that this attenuating influence plays an important role during the focusing of attention in perception, and that a means has thus been provided for the reticular formation for controlling its own afferent input.

Hernandez-Peon's initial investigations were also centered around the effects of attention upon afferent impulses. Some interesting findings reported by Hernandez-Peon, Scheerer, and Jouvet were prefaced by the remark that, "Attention involves the selective awareness of certain sensory messages with the simultaneous suppression of others" (1956, p. 331). Three types of stimuli were used in this investigation to attract the attention of his cats. These were visual, olfactory, and somatic. The now famous situation employed was that the evoked potentials to clicks were measured by means of chronically implanted electrodes at various points in the auditory pathway. Subsequently, during the presentation of the auditory stimulus, two mice in a jar were set before the subject. It was observed that during the presentation of the visual stimulus the evoked potentials to the auditory stimulus were greatly reduced in comparison to the control potentials. Furthermore, they remained suppressed as long as the visual stimulus was present, but when the mice were removed, the auditory response returned to its original magnitude. Other modalities provided the same competing reactions.

Additional data not to be ignored in investigating the mechanisms of habituation come from the recent research in psychopharmacology (Killam & Killam, 1958) and a comparison of the actions of some of the tranquilizing drugs, notably chlorpromazine and reserpine, with anesthetics such as pentobarbital. Hernandez-Peon reports, "A remarkable observation common to all these experiments is that afferent neuronal habituation is released and prevented by barbiturate anesthetics" (1961, p. 510). Sharpless and Jasper state in their experiment, "The use of sedatives and hypnotics proved impracticable, since it was impossible to maintain the delicate adjustment required over a sufficiently long period of time to compare the effects of successive stimuli" (1956, p. 658). These same authors report identical results due to extensive lesions of the mesencephalic reticular formation.

Killam and Killam report that pentobarbital generally depresses the reticular formation to the extent that attention and consciousness are interrupted. According to their investigations, pentobarbital anesthesia, "depressed both cochlear and geniculate responses to clicks and increased the threshold at which reticular stimulation altered the sensory potentials." This supports the findings of Hernandez-Peon and Sharpless and Jasper, and substantiates the role of reticular control over afferent pathways. In the same experiment, Killam and Killam report that following the administration of chlorpromazine, the inhibitory effect of reticular stimulation upon the auditory pathway was enhanced. They state, "These data indicate that chlorpromazine may essentially increase the 'filtering band width' of the reticular formation" (1958, p. 119). Killam and Killam conclude by saying:

> From these data it appears that chlorpromazine acts oppositely from pentobarbital on reticular mechanisms. Thus, two different mechanisms may explain behavioral depression by the two compounds. Pentobarbital appears generally to depress the reticular formation to the point at which attention and consciousness are disturbed. Chlorpromazine on the other hand, increases reticular input and conduction and enhances the controlling or filtering effects of the reticular formation on lateral sensory pathways with little effect on the reticular mechanisms of consciousness (p. 120).

Hence it can be stated that while habituation may be prevented by pentobarbital anesthesia, it may be facilitated by agents such as chlorpromazine. This is because the former blocks interneuronal transmission in the reticular formation while the latter has no such effect. Both produce the result of increasing the threshold for behavioral arousal, but by different actions; pentobarbital because of reduced attention, and chlorpromazine because of facilitated attenuation or selective filtering of sensory input.

A great deal of attention has thus been paid to the neurophysiological mechanisms and substrates of the process of habituation. The results of this research have been inconclusive in many respects, and none of the investigations have been concerned with the behavioral aspects of habituation. While there is a necessity for specifying the neurological mechanisms which can produce such effects, the meaning and nature of the process in terms of behavior are more fundamental problems of concern to psychology.

An analogy can be drawn between traditional avoidance conditioning and the process of habituation. Basically, the process may be considered to be identical to the classical conditioning procedures in which the striate contraction in the dog's leg is elicited by a conditional stimulus in order to avoid a shock to the foot. Likewise, conditional stimuli may come to elicit responses to avoid aversive, monotonous, or insignificant stimuli.

To elaborate upon this point, it is also necessary to state that there are a number of ways of looking at conditioned avoidance behavior. Examples from classical conditioning are techniques used in which it is typical that the sound of a metronome is paired with an electric shock to the animal's foreleg. At first, only the shock (US) will elicit a flexion of the leg muscles, but after a few trials the beat of the metronome will evoke an anticipatory avoidance response. Pavlov's defensive reflex of conditioning a salivation response with acid in the mouth as the unconditioned stimulus is of the same type. Salivation, in this case, is instrumental in avoiding the noxious acid by diluting it (Woodworth & Schlosberg, 1954). Extensions of classically conditioned avoidance responses are numerous. Another reflex similar to this, which has been used in a great many conditioning studies with humans and animals, is the eye blink. In the typical experiment, the subject has his head in a rest, and in front of his eyes is a lighted patch, a change in the brightness of which represents the conditioned stimulus. A puff of air to the cornea of the eye serves as the unconditioned stimulus and results in a reflexive eye wink. It has been shown many times that if a light or other stimulus preceded the puff of air, an anticipatory blink develops because, as Woodworth and Schlosberg state, "This wink is rewarded in that it keeps the puff of air off the sensitive cornea" (p. 553).

These classically conditioned avoidance responses seem to be just as instrumental as those of running from one compartment of a box to another, pushing on a panel to avoid shock, or the operant response of a bar press to a discriminative stimulus. In any case, the conditioned response allows the subject to avoid an aversive stimulus of some sort which does not necessarily need to be painful to be aversive. The efferent response of the eye to a sudden light or puff of air is basically the same as the efferent responses in the ear through the effector of the striate muscles of the middle ear (Galambos & Rupert, 1959), the efferent suppression of auditory nerve activity (Galambos, 1956), or the efferent control of transmission at successively higher relay points of the auditory pathway (Hernandez-Peon & Scheerer, 1955; Hernandez-Peon, Scheerer, & Jouvet, 1956). The efferent response of the ear is no different in the case of habituation from that of the eye except that it cannot be so easily observed or measured. Even though the response of a receptor as a result of conditioned avoidance is not a skeletal movement as in running, jumping, or bar pressing, the result is functionally similar. It avoids aversive stimulation and, as such, is basically instrumental behavior.

A position which might be legitimately adopted is that an irrelevant stimulus is just as aversive to the central nervous system as a noxious one. An irrelevant repetitive stimulus, economically, demands activation of various receptors, pathways, relay nuclei, and cortical areas which is a waste of energy and an extravagant expense which it need not afford. The highly selective process of habituation allows the central nervous system to avoid activation by insignificant and irrelevant stimulation by efferent responses at a number of points within each receptor system. Sokolov (1960) has even demonstrated that this selective attenuation applies also to compound stimuli involving multiple receptor systems and to harmonic tonal patterns. Any minute change in the stimulus parameters, of course, results in the reappearance of the orienting reflex or arousal response. Indeed, this form of conditioned avoidance behavior in terms of selective attenuation of irrelevant stimuli is more exact than other types of conditioned responses since generalization, if such occurs at all, must be confined to extremely narrow limits. In his most recent review of his own and other Russian investigations of the orienting reflex, Sokolov has interpreted his findings as representing the establishment of a state of conditioned inhibition within the central nervous system which modifies or blocks afferent input. However, the demonstrations of Hernandez-Peon and Galambos would seem to indicate a conditioned avoidance hypothesis, which carries with it the assumption of an active efferent response within the mechanisms of the receptor or at any one of its successively higher relay nuclei including the cortex.

The key to determining which hypothesis is correct probably lies in the rate of presentation of the repeated signal (McDaniel & White, 1966). Sokolov seems correct in his analogy, "Both extinction of the orienting reflex and conditioned inhibition develop proportionally to the number of times the stimulus is applied" (1963, p. 561). On the other hand, different rates of the establishment of habituation attributable to varying the periodicity of the stimulus when frequency, duration, intensity and the number of repetitions are held constant favor an active process of conditioned avoidance rather than conditioned inhibition (McDaniel & White). At least partial support for these interpretations has also been provided by the studies of Fox (1964), Lubow and Moore (1959), and Lubow (1965).

This detailed discussion of novel stimulation, attention, habituation, and learning should adequately illustrate the important role of these factors in normal behavior regulation and control. It follows that any physical damage or disability which interferes with perceptual processes also interferes with training and performances. Moreover, there are many extraneous influences which could interfere with treatment and rehabilitation if perceptual processes are disturbed. All of the variables previously mentioned in regard to perception, emotion, and motivation are capable of modifying attention, habituation, and therefore the performance of patients in any sort of therapeutic situation.

Without belaboring the issues any further, I would like to recommend to future investigators in the area of the psychological aspects of physical illness and disability that we become more concerned with variables of intrinsic control and emphasize much less the study of psychopathological and social consequences of physiological impairments. I would recommend to clinicians of all types, too, that they attempt to divert their concern from defects and deficits to maximizing regulation and control potentials.

References

Butler, R. Discrimination learning by rhesus monkeys to visual exploration motivation. *J. Comp. Physiol. Psy.*, 1953, **46**, 95-8.

Estes, W. K. Toward a statistical theory of learning. *Psy. Rev.*, 1950, **57**, 94-107.

Ferster, C. & Skinner, B.   *Schedules of Reinforcement.* 1957, Appleton-Century, New York.

Fox, S. Evoked potential habituation rate and sensory pattern preference as determined by stimulus information. *J. Comp. Physiol. Psy.*, 1964, **58**, 225-32.

Galambos, R. Suppression of auditory nerve activity by stimulation of efferent fibers to cochlea. *J. Neurophysiol.*, 1956, **19**, 424-37.

Galambos, R. Studies of the auditory system with implanted electrodes. In *Neural Mechanisms of the Auditory and Vestibular Systems.* (Rasmussen & Windle, Eds.) 1960, Thomas, Springfield, Ill.

Galambos, R. & Rupert, A. Action of the middle ear muscles in normal cats. *J. Acous. Soc. Am.*, 1959, **31**, 349-55.

Galambos, R., Sheatz, G., & Vernier, V.   Electrophysiological correlates of a conditioned response in cats. *Science*, 1956, **123**, 376-7.

Gastaut, H. Etude topographique des reactions electroencephalographiques conditionees chez l'homme. *EEG and Clin. Neurophysiol.*, 1957, **8**, 1-34.

Gastaut, H. The role of the reticular formation in establishing conditioned reactions. In *Reticular Formation of the Brain.* (Jasper, Ed.) 1958, Little, Brown, Boston.

Gootzeit, J. Effecting communication and interaction in the severely retarded. *J. Rehab.*, 1967, **31**, 16-22.

Harlow, H. Learning and satiation of response in intrinsically motivated complex puzzle performance by monkeys. *J. Comp. Physiol. Psy.*, 1950, **43**, 289-94.

Hernandez-Peon, R. Reticular mechanisms of sensory control. In *Sensory Communication.* 1961, M.I.T., Cambridge, Mass.

Hernandez-Peon, R. & Scheerer, H. Habituation to acoustic stimuli in the cochlear nucleus. *Fed. Proc.,* 1955, **14**, 71.

Hernandez-Peon, R., Scheerer, H., & Jouvet, M. Modification of electrical activity in cochlear nucleus during "attention" in unanesthetized cats. *Science,* 1956, **123**, 331-2.

Jasper, H. and Penfield, W. *Epilepsy and the Functional Anatomy of the Human Brain.* 1954, Little, Brown, Boston.

Killam, D. & Killam, E. Drug action on pathways involving the reticular formation. In *Reticular Formation of the Brain.* (Jasper, Ed.) 1958, Little, Brown, Boston.

Lubow R. & Moore, A. Latent inhibition: The effect of nonreinforced pre-exposure to the conditional stimulus. *J. Comp. Physiol. Psychol.,* 1959, **52**, 415-19.

Lubow, R. Latent inhibition: Effects of frequency of nonreinforced preexposure of the conditional stimulus. *J. Comp. Physiol. Psychol.,* 1965, **60**, 454-7.

McBain, W. Noise, the "arousal hypothesis" and monotonous work. *J. Appl. Psy.,* 1961, **45**, 309-17.

McDaniel, J. & White, R. A factorial study of the stimulus conditions of habituation. *Percept. Mot. Skills,* 1966, **23**, 259-70.

Marsh, J., McCarthy, D., Sheatz, G., & Galambos, R. Amplitude changes in evoked potentials during habituation and conditioning. *EEG and Clin. Neurophysiol.,* 1961, **13**, 224-34.

Martin, Irene. Adaptation. *Psychol. Bull.,* 1964, **61**, 35-45.

Montgomery, K. The role of the exploratory drive in learning. *J. Comp. Physiol. Psych.*, 1954, **47**, 60-4.

Montgomery, K. The relation between fear induced by novel stimulation and exploratory behavior. *J. Comp. Physiol. Psych.*, 1955, **48**.

Mowrer, O. H. *Learning Theory and Behavior.* 1960, Wiley, New York.

Pavlov, I. P. *Conditioned Reflexes.* 1927, Oxford, London.

Pribram, K. The new neurology: **Memory**, novelty, thought, and choice. *EEG and Behavior.* 1963, Basic Books, New York.

Sharpless, S. and Jasper, H. Habituation of the arousal reaction. *Brain*, 1956, **79**, 655-80.

Shontz, F. Somatopsychology: Concept and content. *Bull. APA Div. 22*, 1965, **12**, 20-7.

Skinner, B. F. *The Behavior of Organisms.* 1938, Appleton-Century, New York.

Sokolov, E.N. Neuronal models and the orienting reflex. In *The Central Nervous System and Behavior.* (Brazier, Ed.) 1960, Macy Foundation, New York.

Sokolov, E. N. Higher nervous functions: The orienting reflex. *Ann. Rev. Physiol.*, 1963, **25**, 545-600.

Woodworth, R. and Schlosberg, H. *Experimental Psychology.* 1954, Holt, New York.

SUBJECT
INDEX

A

Ability
and motivation in performance 134-6

Achievement
American values 11
motives 134-6

Aging
and performance 179-80

Amputation
body-image 8
body image research 95,97
mastectomy 94
phantom pain 65
phantom perceptions 99-104
vertical perception 113-14, 125

Anxiety
motivation 142-3
psychoendocrine studies 77-8
situational stresses 60

Arousal
and hospital adjustment 60-3
bodily perceptions 91
motivation level 140-2
pain 65-7
regulation of behavior 207

Arthritis
personality studies 50, 69

Attention
changes with illness 50-2
information processing 206-7
sensory compensation 105-6

Attitudes
age and 24-5
ATDP scale 18-21
family members' 38-40
of employers 33-8
prejudice 18-22, 27
professional 41-3
toward disabilities 22-3, 28
toward disabled 17-32

B

Blindness
attitudes concerning 21-2, 24
depression and glaucoma 73
occupation performance 192-3
removal of disability 82
sensory compensation 104-7
sensory restriction 57-9, 68

Body-Image
attitudes toward disabled 28-30
body part preferences 31-2
emotional reactions 50-4
perceptual processes 89-99
Schilder's Theory 7-9
size judgments 93-4

C

Cardiac Disease
depressive reactions 74-5
disability 79
family problems 40
hiring practices 36-7
performance 180, 191
surgical response 82, 149